D1373127

THINK BOOK

Visually Oriented Problem-Solving Activities

by Linda Nayes Brown

Incentive Publications, Inc.
Nashville, Tennessee

Cover by Janet Levine March
Edited by Sally Sharpe

ISBN 0-86530-087-9

© 1990 by Incentive Publications, Inc. All rights reserved. No part of this publication may be reproduced, stored in a retrieval system, or transmitted in any form or by any means (electronic, mechanical, photocopying, recording or otherwise) without prior written permission from Incentive Publications, Inc. with the exception below:

Permission is hereby granted to the purchaser to reproduce, in sufficient quantities for meeting yearly classroom needs, pages bearing the following statement: © 1990 by Incentive Publications, Inc., Nashville, TN.

Table of Contents

FIGURAL RELATIONSHIPS

LOGICAL REASONING

AESTHETIC/INTUITIVE RELATIONSHIPS

PROPORTIONAL/SPATIAL RELATIONSHIPS

VISUAL/SPATIAL RELATIONSHIPS

APPENDIX

INTRODUCTION

THINK BOOK contains problem-solving activities for grades 1-6 which promote active thinking from basic visual discrimination and grouping to the logical thinking patterns of inductive and deductive reasoning. All of the activities are visually (figurally) oriented and require mental manipulation of varying degrees with few reading and math calculation skills required.

Although critical and creative thinking are necessary and integral parts of the content areas, the activities in this book seek to remove as many barriers as possible which are imposed by written/verbal communication and/or mathematical calculation. This allows the individual to give maximum attention to the reasoning process itself. Whenever possible (as *you* see fit), the activities can be used to enhance or build upon related thinking skills in every dimension of classroom learning.

Both critical and creative problem-solving activities have been included. Critical thinking involves the use of basic reasoning skills and logical thinking patterns to resolve unknown difficulties. Creative thinking goes beyond the critical to include intuition and imagination in inventing novel aesthetic or practical solutions to known or unknown difficulties. Although many of the activities require convergent responses, you should encourage creative suggestions and strategies for solving the problems. Promote calculated risk-taking by demonstrating respect for the reasonable consideration of students' divergent thoughts. Such acceptance promotes independent thinking and eases the tension of publicly sharing "questionable" ideas.

Several of the activities have variable outcomes. If a student can justify his or her response, then that student should be praised for going beyond analysis and synthesis to the higher process of self-evaluation and personal accountability. Praise students' efforts rather than their specific responses. Use acceptance, expansion or clarification techniques to enhance rather than stifle the exploration of a topic. (Note: Although praise is never a destructive response, it can have a limiting effect. Praise often terminates a discussion through the assumption that a "correct" answer has been given.)

Most of the activities may be worked individually. However, by using the activities in group situations, students will verbalize their thoughts and thus create a whole new dimension of learning. Your role in presenting the activities is to introduce (define) the problem, to give directions and to relate the desired outcomes. After the students have attempted to solve the problems, lead a discussion of the proposed solutions using higher level questioning to promote metacognition ("thinking about thinking").

Example questions: What made you think . . . ?
Why do you think . . . ?
What if . . . ?
Suppose that . . . ?

Through this process, students not only will perform the cognitive processes of thinking, but they also will be guided back into their thoughts to discover their paths of reasoning. Your insight and creative questioning will enable students to become aware of the usefulness of knowing such patterns for future reference.

Always remember that solving unknown problems or searching for novel approaches to problems is a vulnerable position which requires intellectual and social risk-taking. Listen to the students and take the time to encourage and support the generation of individual and original thoughts and judgments. After all, that is the whole purpose of thinking!

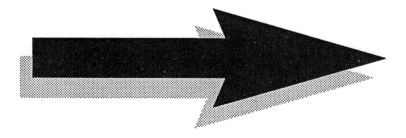

* Note: Activities bearing the ⬤**Challenge** symbol are more difficult and require the use of higher thinking skills.

The Order of Thinking

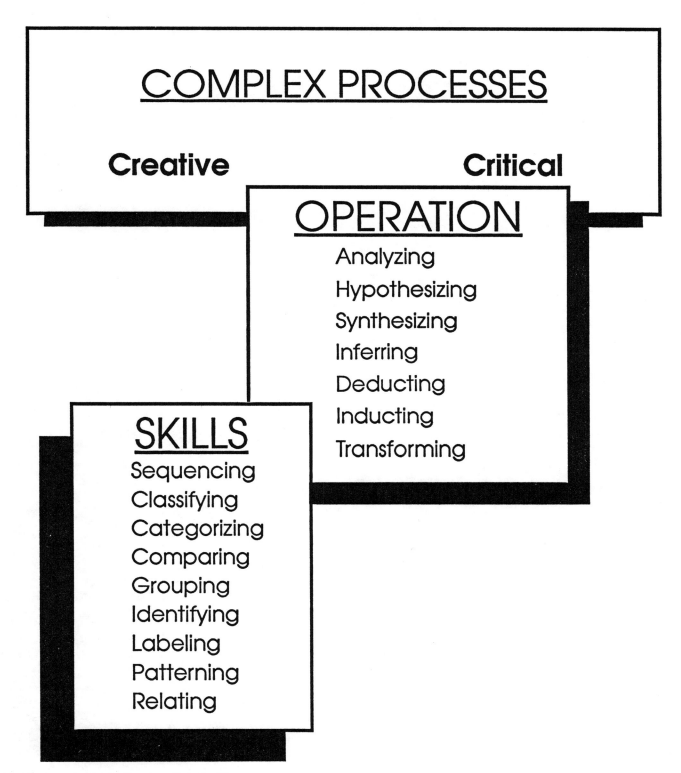

COMPLEX PROCESSES

Creative   **Critical**

OPERATION
Analyzing
Hypothesizing
Synthesizing
Inferring
Deducting
Inducting
Transforming

SKILLS
Sequencing
Classifying
Categorizing
Comparing
Grouping
Identifying
Labeling
Patterning
Relating

© 1989 by Incentive Publications, Inc., Nashville, TN.

ABOUT WARMING UP

Never say never ... never say it isn't possible. There are always new ways to look at problems. There are always new ways to look at our·surroundings, the things we do without thinking, and the things we take for granted. Both critical and creative problem-solving evolve from an open, active mind.

During physical activities, the body functions more efficiently if it has been "warmed up," and it becomes more adept with practice. The same is true for thinking activities. By practicing divergent thinking and logical reasoning, the mind is tuned in to those thought patterns – attitude and imagination are sparked with creative energy.

The following seven pages contain a variety of warmup exercises for the mind and the senses. Use these activities before beginning more involved thinking exercises.

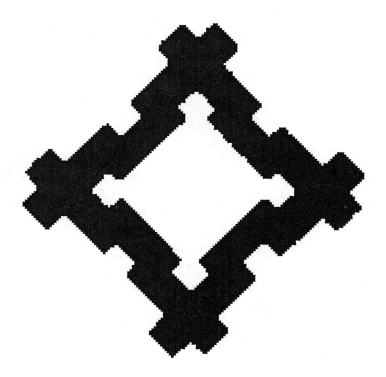

WARMING UP I

The Problem: Getting students to think about "things they do without thinking."

The Activity: Have the students think about and answer these questions:

What did you have for lunch yesterday?

What is the first thing you said this morning?

What is the last thing you said last night?

Which hand do you raise to answer a question in school *(try to answer before you do it)*?

What color socks are you wearing right now *(don't look!)*?

How many people did you see on your way to school this morning *(students not included)*?

When was the last time you wore a bandage? What happened?

How many trees are in your yard at home?

Who took the most recent picture of you? Where were you? Was anyone with you? Who?

What is your mom or dad's favorite restaurant?

How many sides does a stop sign have?

Which color is on the top of a traffic light?

Look around the room. What three things have you never noticed before?

What color is the sky today?

What food smells the best to you *(smell, not taste)*?

What food tastes the best to you?

Imagine that you are feeling something slippery and slimy. What is it?

Imagine that you are feeling something scratchy. What is it?

How many kids in our class wear glasses *(don't look!)*?

Imagine that a waiter just brought a hot pizza to your table. What does it smell like? What toppings are on it?

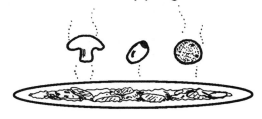

Imagine that you just took a batch of hot cookies out of the oven. What do they smell like? What kind of cookies are they? Imagine that you tried to eat one before it cooled. How does your tongue feel?

Imagine that your mom or dad just made a fresh pot of coffee. What does it smell like? Do you like the smell?

Imagine that someone is boiling a pot of cabbage. What does it smell like? Do you like the smell? Imagine that you are tasting it. Do you like the taste?

Imagine that you caught a fish and left it in the hot car all afternoon. What does the car smell like? Will you eat the fish when you get home? Why or why not?

Imagine that you just walked into your favorite fast food restaurant. What do you smell? What will you order and why?

Imagine that you are petting a tiny kitten. What does it feel like?

Close your eyes and listen for three minutes. What do you hear? *(Try this inside and outside.)*

How does a person's voice change when he or she is angry, excited or sad?

How do a person's eyes change when he or she is angry, excited, sad or tired?

How does a person's mouth change when he or she is angry, excited or sad?

WARMING UP II

The Problem: Using divergent thinking skills.

The Activity: Ask the students to think of as many uses as they can for the following things (other than conventional answers).

> Example: A rock
> ... a paperweight
> ... a sculpture
> ... a weapon
> ... a spice crusher
> ... etc.

- a bandage
- a paper clip
- a piece of paper
- a brick
- an apple
- a corncob
- a glass of water
- a small table
- a large table
- a pencil
- a newspaper
- a bandanna
- a cracker
- a picture frame

- a crayon
- a towel
- a wagon
- a cardboard box
- a tractor tire (not on a tractor)

WARMING UP III

The Problem: Using divergent thinking skills.

The Activity: Give the directions for the following 26 thinking problems.

A. Instruct the students to draw nine dots on a piece of paper (draw an example on the board). Then instruct the students to draw through all nine dots, without lifting their pencils, by using only four straight lines.

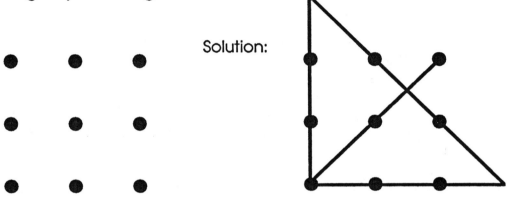

Solution:

B. Ask all of the students except one to close their eyes. That one student should make a sound using something in the room (tapping a pencil, writing with chalk, etc.). Ask the group to guess "what" the sound is.

C. Put three different kinds of pencils in a bag. Ask each of three students to choose a pencil, without looking at it, and to feel it. Then, instruct the students to put the pencils into the bag. Take the pencils out of the bag and ask each student to identify the pencil he or she selected. (This activity can be done with many different small objects. The more objects there are, the more difficult it will be!)

D. Ask each student to choose a color and to list all of the things in his or her room at home that are that color.

E. Select a word from the dictionary that the students do not know and write a brief definition of the word. Read the word to the class and have each student write a definition for the word. Read all of the definitions to the group and ask the students to choose the best one.

F. Read this riddle to the class and ask the students to solve it. Amy went to the dentist to have her teeth cleaned. Amy is the dentist's daughter, but the dentist is not Amy's father. How can this be? *(Answer: The dentist is Amy's mother.)*

G. Read the following riddle to the class and then ask for a solution. Jimmy was crossing the street near his house when he was hit by a car. His father was home and rushed him to the hospital. When they took Jimmy in for surgery, the doctor cried, "Oh, no! I can't operate on him. He's my son!" How can this be? *(Answer: The doctor is Jimmy's mother.)*

H. Have the students cut pictures of people out of different kinds of magazines. Ask each student to choose a picture and to imagine what that person is like. Ask questions such as these. Do you think you would like this person? Do you think this person likes sports? If so, what kinds? Do you think this person does or did well in school? What makes you think these things? Is it his or her clothes, facial expression, actions, etc.?

I. Ask each student to examine the face of a cartoon character, before reading the cartoon, and to determine the mood of the character. Then instruct the student to read the cartoon to find out if he or she was right.

J. Ask the students to solve this riddle. How can two people stand face-to-face on one piece of newspaper and not be able to touch each other? *(Answer: Slide the news-paper under a door and have one person stand on each side of the door.)*

K. Let students take turns supplying answers for this riddle. You have five tiny pieces of paper on the palm of your hand. How can you blow them off one by one? *(Answer: Use a straw or cover all but one piece with your hand—one at a time.)*

L. Write this riddle on the board and let the students offer their solutions. There is a penny in a hole. The hole is only a little wider than the coin, and it is deeper than your arm. How can you get the penny out of the hole? *(Answer: Put a piece of tape on the end of a stick and use the stick to retrieve the penny.)*

M. Ask each student to make four triangles with equal sides using only six toothpicks. *(Answer: Break all six toothpicks in half and make four separate triangles.)*

N. Show a picture to the class and ask the students to list all of the things that might be happening. *(Example: A picture of a woman "walking a dog": Is the woman walking the dog or is the dog really pulling the woman? Is the woman going somewhere or is she on her way home?)*

O. Have the students think about this problem. How can you empty a glass of water that is "resting" on a table without touching the glass or the table? Encourage the students to think of more than one answer. *(Possible Answers: Drink the water through a straw. Use forceps to pick up the glass and turn it over. Cover the glass with a cloth before turning it over. Etc.)*

P. Let students experiment to solve this problem. You have six glasses. Three of the glasses are full of water and three are empty. Line up the glasses so that the three full glasses are next to each other and the three empty glasses are next to each other. Then, by changing only one glass, arrange them so that no full glass is next to another full glass and no empty glass is next to another empty glass.

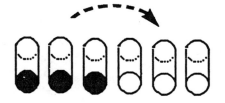

(Answer: Pour the second full glass into the second empty glass.)

Q. Challenge the students with this riddle. You have two pails. One pail holds six quarts and the other holds four quarts. You need exactly two quarts. What do you do? *(Answer: Fill the six-quart pail and then use it to fill the four-quart pail. Then you will have exactly two quarts left in the six-quart pail.)*

R. Ask the students to answer this riddle. A girl's grandmother is only seven years older than her mother. How can this be? *(Answer: The grandmother is the girl's father's mother.)*

S. Students will enjoy answering this riddle. Today at the beach Jane collected a frog, a pretty rock and a fly. Which one was missing when Jan got home? Why do you think so? *(Answer: The fly is missing because the frog ate it.)*

T. Give the following facts to the students and ask them to answer the question. Jane can draw dogs, but she draws sloppy cats. Don can draw nice dogs and horses. Cathy can draw cats and dogs. Which two people should work together to draw a nice picture of cats and horses? *(Answer: Don and Cathy)*

U. Let the class solve this riddle. At the pet shop downtown, dogs sell better than either cats or hamsters, but not as well as fish, which sell best at the shop at the mall. Leashes do not outsell cats, but they outsell gerbils. What is the downtown pet shop's poorest-selling item? *(Answer: Gerbils)*

V. Ask the students to answer this riddle. Two boys played chess. They played seven games and won the same number of games. How can this be? *(Answer: The boys each won three games and tied one game (stalemate).)*

W. Have the students draw pictures on paper or the board to solve this riddle. How can a cake be cut into eight equal pieces with only three cuts?

top view side view *(Answer: Two cuts on the top and one cut through the middle.)*

X. See which student is first to give the correct answer to this riddle. A woman gives a beggar 50 cents. The woman is the beggar's sister, but the beggar is not the woman's brother. How can this be? *(Answer: The beggar is the woman's sister.)*

Y. This simple riddle often stumps students. A farmer had 17 sheep. All but three died. How many sheep did the farmer have left? *(Answer: Three)*

Z. Some months have 30 days. Some have 31 days. How many months have 28 days? *(Answer: All)*

SPACES AND PLACES: OPEN/CLOSED

The Problem: Visually discriminating between open and closed figures.

The Activity: Reproduce and distribute pages 20-22. Instruct the students to color all closed figures and to cross out all open figures.

PROCESS/SKILLS CHART

Complex Process
Critical Thinking
Creative Thinking

Thought Scheme
✓ **Convergent Thinking**
Divergent Thinking

Content Skills
Reading Skills Required
Writing Skills Required
Counting Skills Required

Basic Skills
✓ **Analysis**
Categorizing
Classifying
✓ **Comparison**

Conditional Logic
Deductive Reasoning
Grouping
Hypothesizing
✓ **Identification**
Imagination
Inductive Reasoning
Inference
Intuition
Labeling
Logical Reasoning
Originality
Part to Whole Relationships
Patterning
✓ **Relationships (Visual)**
Sequencing
Spatial Relationships
Synthesis
Transformations

Notes:

SPACES AND PLACES: OPEN/CLOSED I

Color all closed figures.
Cross out all open figures.

Closed

Open

© 1990 by Incentive Publications, Inc., Nashville, TN.

* Answer Key

SPACES AND PLACES: OPEN/CLOSED II

Color all closed figures.
Cross out all open figures.

 Closed

 Open

© 1990 by Incentive Publications, Inc., Nashville, TN.

* Answer Key

Name _____

SPACES AND PLACES: OPEN/CLOSED III

Color all closed figures.
Cross out all open figures.

Closed

Open

© 1990 by Incentive Publications, Inc., Nashville, TN.

* Answer Key

SPACES AND PLACES: INSIDE/OUTSIDE

The Problem: Visually discriminating between "inside" and "outside" in nonrepresentational figures.

The Activity: Reproduce and distribute pages 24-26. Instruct the students to color all of the figures with a dot "inside" and to cross out all of the figures with a dot "outside."

PROCESS/SKILLS CHART

Complex Process
  Critical Thinking
  Creative Thinking

Thought Scheme
  ✓ **Convergent Thinking**
  Divergent Thinking

Content Skills
  Reading Skills Required
  Writing Skills Required
  Counting Skills Required

Basic Skills
  ✓ **Analysis**
  Categorizing
  Classifying
  ✓ **Comparison**

Conditional Logic
Deductive Reasoning
Grouping
Hypothesizing
✓ **Identification**
Imagination
Inductive Reasoning
Inference
Intuition
Labeling
Logical Reasoning
Originality
Part to Whole Relationships
Patterning
✓ **Relationships (Visual)**
Sequencing
✓ **Spatial Relationships**
Synthesis
Transformations

Notes:

SPACES AND PLACES: INSIDE/OUTSIDE I

Color each figure with a dot inside.

Cross out each figure with a dot outside.

dot inside

dot outside

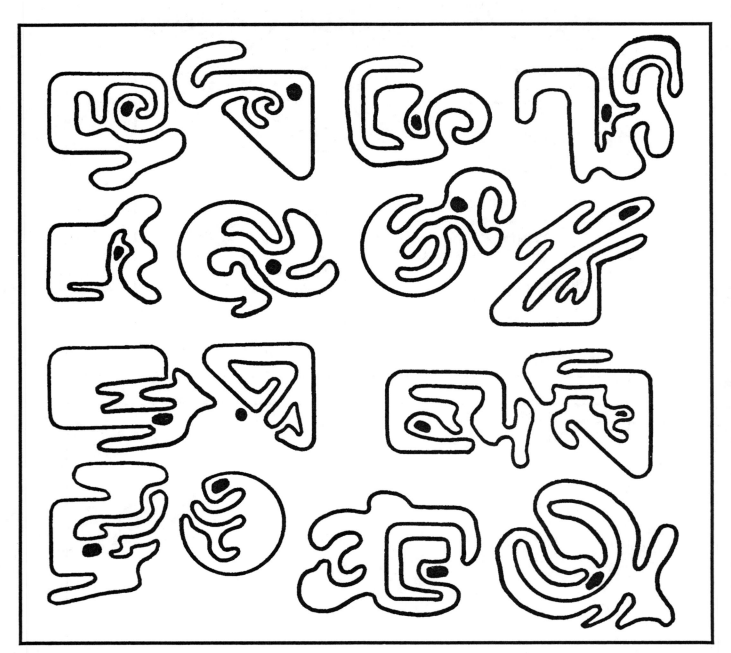

© 1990 by Incentive Publications, Inc., Nashville, TN.

* Answer Key

SPACES AND PLACES: OPEN/CLOSED II

Color each figure with a dot
   inside.
Cross out each figure with a dot
   outside.

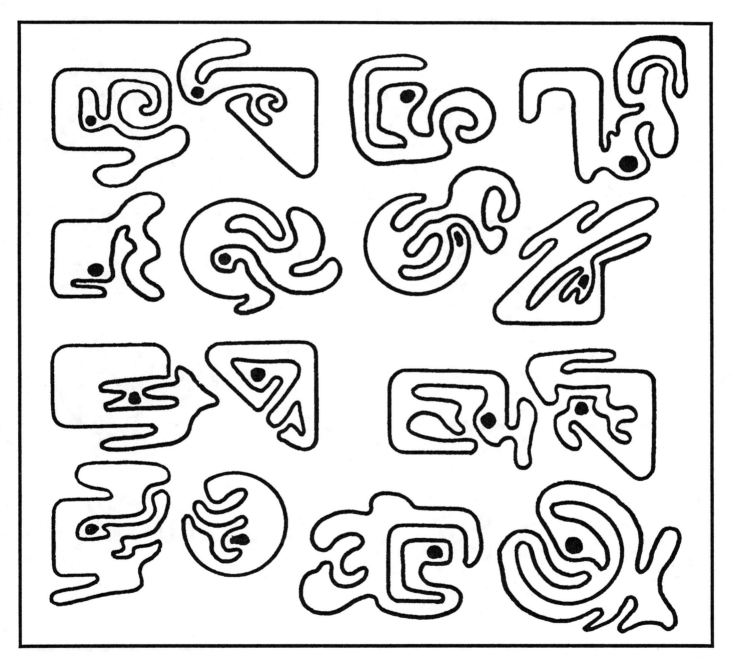

© 1990 by Incentive Publications, Inc., Nashville, TN.

* Answer Key

SPACES AND PLACES: OPEN/CLOSED III

Color each figure with a dot
   inside.
Cross out each figure with a dot
   outside.

dot
inside

dot
outside

© 1990 by Incentive Publications, Inc., Nashville, TN.

* Answer Key

SPACES AND PLACES: CONNECT-THE-DOTS

The Problem: Visually discriminating between "inside" and "outside" and noting the relationship of two objects.

The Activity: Reproduce and distribute pages 28-30. Instruct the students to connect the two dots in each figure only if it can be done without crossing any lines.

PROCESS/SKILLS CHART

Complex Process
Critical Thinking
Creative Thinking

Thought Scheme
✓ **Convergent Thinking**
Divergent Thinking

Content Skills
Reading Skills Required
Writing Skills Required
Counting Skills Required

Basic Skills
✓ **Analysis**
Categorizing
Classifying
✓ **Comparison**

Conditional Logic
Deductive Reasoning
Grouping
Hypothesizing
✓ **Identification**
Imagination
Inductive Reasoning
Inference
Intuition
Labeling
Logical Reasoning
Originality
Part to Whole Relationships
Patterning
✓ **Relationships (Visual)**
Sequencing
✓ **Spatial Relationships**
Synthesis
Transformations

Notes:

SPACES AND PLACES: CONNECT-THE-DOTS I

can't
connect

Connect the two dots in each figure only if you can do it without crossing any lines.

© 1990 by Incentive Publications, Inc., Nashville, TN.

* Answer Key

Name _____

SPACES AND PLACES: CONNECT-THE-DOTS II

can't
connect

Connect the two dots in each figure only if you can do it without crossing any lines.

© 1990 by Incentive Publications, Inc., Nashville, TN.

* Answer Key

SPACES AND PLACES: CONNECT-THE-DOTS III

Connect the two dots in each figure only if you can do it without crossing any lines.

© 1990 by Incentive Publications, Inc., Nashville, TN.

* Answer Key

SPACES AND PLACES: SHARED SPACE

The Problem: Visually discriminating the spatial relationship of two or more figures.

The Activity: Reproduce and distribute pages 32 and 33. Instruct the students to color all of the spaces that the figures share.

PROCESS/SKILLS CHART

Complex Process
Critical Thinking
Creative Thinking

Thought Scheme
✓ **Convergent Thinking**
Divergent Thinking

Content Skills
Reading Skills Required
Writing Skills Required
Counting Skills Required

Basic Skills
✓ **Analysis**
Categorizing
Classifying
✓ **Comparison**

Conditional Logic
Deductive Reasoning
Grouping
Hypothesizing
✓ **Identification**
Imagination
Inductive Reasoning
Inference
Intuition
Labeling
Logical Reasoning
Originality
Part to Whole Relationships
Patterning
✓ **Relationships (Visual)**
Sequencing
✓ **Spatial Relationships**
Synthesis
Transformations

Notes:

SPACES AND PLACES: SHARED SPACE I

Color all of the spaces that the
figures share.

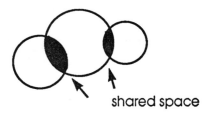

shared space

© 1990 by Incentive Publications, Inc., Nashville, TN.

* Answer Key

SPACES AND PLACES: SHARED SPACE II

Color all of the spaces that the
figures share.

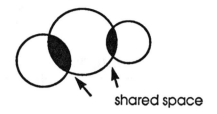

shared space

© 1990 by Incentive Publications, Inc., Nashville, TN.

* Answer Key

SHAPE MATCHING

The Problem: Visually discriminating the relationship of various geometric and/or non-geometric forms.

The Activity: Reproduce and distribute pages 35-37. Instruct the students to match the shapes as directed in each activity.

PROCESS/SKILLS CHART

Complex Process
Critical Thinking
Creative Thinking

Thought Scheme
✓ **Convergent Thinking**
Divergent Thinking

Content Skills
Reading Skills Required
Writing Skills Required
Counting Skills Required

Basic Skills
✓ **Analysis**
Categorizing
Classifying
✓ **Comparison**

Conditional Logic
Deductive Reasoning
Grouping
Hypothesizing
✓ **Identification**
Imagination
Inductive Reasoning
Inference
Intuition
Labeling
Logical Reasoning
Originality
Part to Whole Relationships
Patterning
✓ **Relationships (Visual)**
Sequencing
Spatial Relationships
Synthesis
Transformations

Notes:

SHAPE MATCHING I

Write each letter in the matching shape.

© 1990 by Incentive Publications, Inc., Nashville, TN.

* Answer Key

SHAPE MATCHING II

Write each letter in the matching shape.

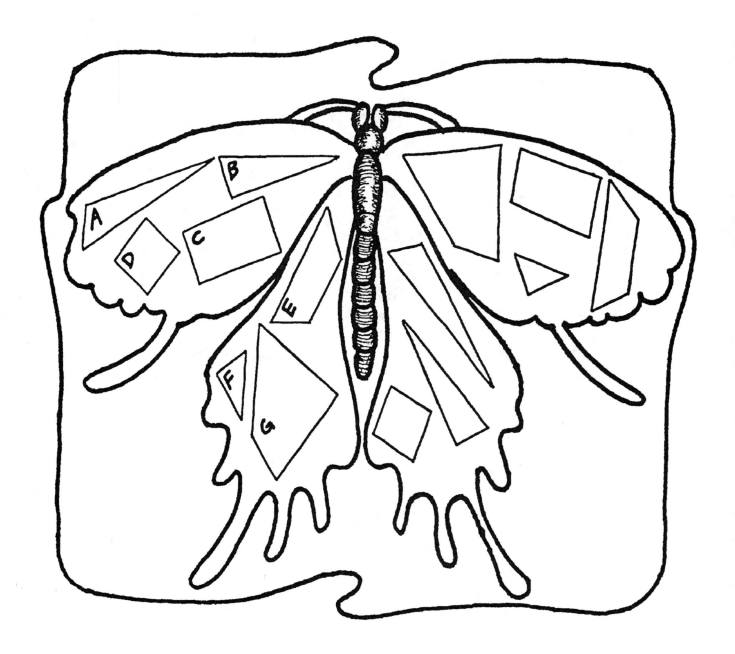

© 1990 by Incentive Publications, Inc., Nashville, TN.

* Answer Key

SHAPE MATCHING III

Find two matching shapes in the butterfly for each letter.
Write each letter in the matching shapes.

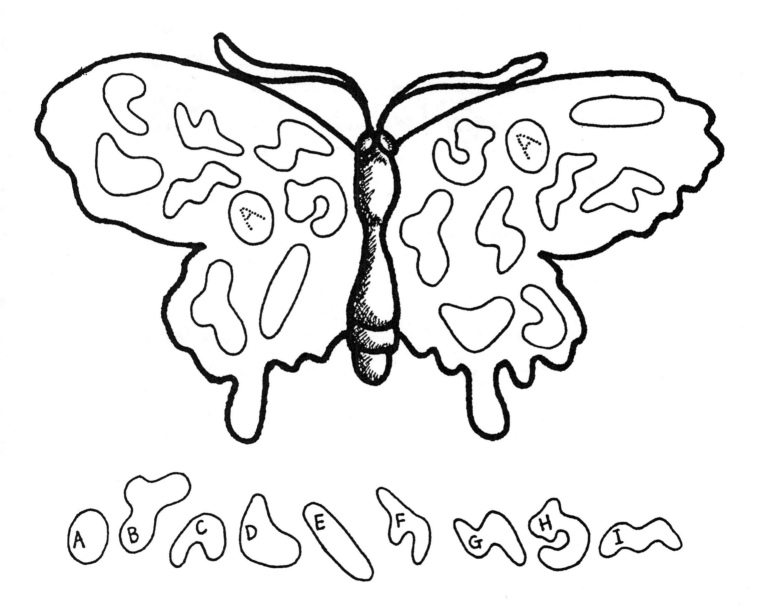

© 1990 by Incentive Publications, Inc., Nashville, TN.

* Answer Key

GEOMETRIC PROBLEMS: TRIANGLES AND RECTANGLES

The Problem: Visually discriminating geometric objects in situations in which it is possible for an individual to go beyond the obvious into the complex.

The Activity: Reproduce and distribute pages 39-44. Instruct the students to count the shapes as directed in each activity.

PROCESS/SKILLS CHART

Complex Process
- ✓ Critical Thinking
- ✓ Creative Thinking

Thought Scheme
- Convergent Thinking
- ✓ Divergent Thinking

Content Skills
- Reading Skills Required
- Writing Skills Required
- ✓ Counting Skills Required

Basic Skills
- ✓ Analysis
- Categorizing
- Classifying
- ✓ Comparison

Conditional Logic
Deductive Reasoning
Grouping
Hypothesizing
- ✓ Identification
Imagination
Inductive Reasoning
Inference
Intuition
Labeling
- ✓ Logical Reasoning
Originality
- ✓ Part to Whole Relationships
Patterning
Relationships (Visual)
Sequencing
- ✓ Spatial Relationships
- ✓ Synthesis
Transformations

Notes:

GEOMETRIC PROBLEMS:
TRIANGLES AND RECTANGLES I

Count the triangles.
Write the number of triangles in each set in the space provided.

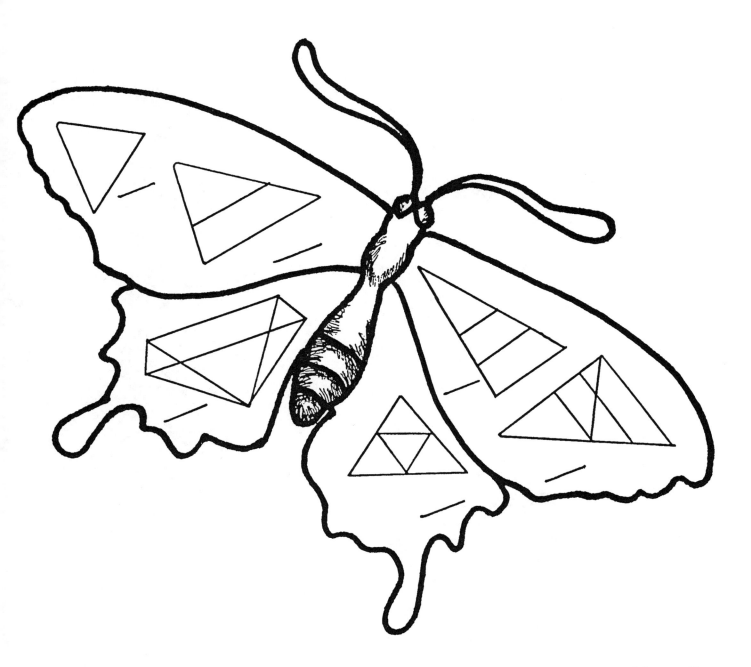

© 1990 by Incentive Publications, Inc., Nashville, TN.

* Answer Key

Challenge

GEOMETRIC PROBLEMS: TRIANGLES AND RECTANGLES II

Count the squares.
Write the number of squares in each set in the space provided.

_____

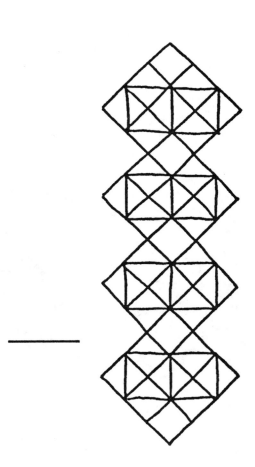

_____

_____

© 1990 by Incentive Publications, Inc., Nashville, TN.

* Answer Key

GEOMETRIC PROBLEMS:
TRIANGLES AND RECTANGLES III

Cut a square, rectangle or triangle out of a piece of paper.
Trace the shape on this page several times.
Touch sides and overlap shapes to make a design.
Then ask a friend to count the number of that shape in the design.

© 1990 by Incentive Publications, Inc., Nashville, TN.

Name _____

GEOMETRIC PROBLEMS:
TRIANGLES AND RECTANGLES IV

How many squares are missing in each numbered space?
Write the answer in the numbered space.

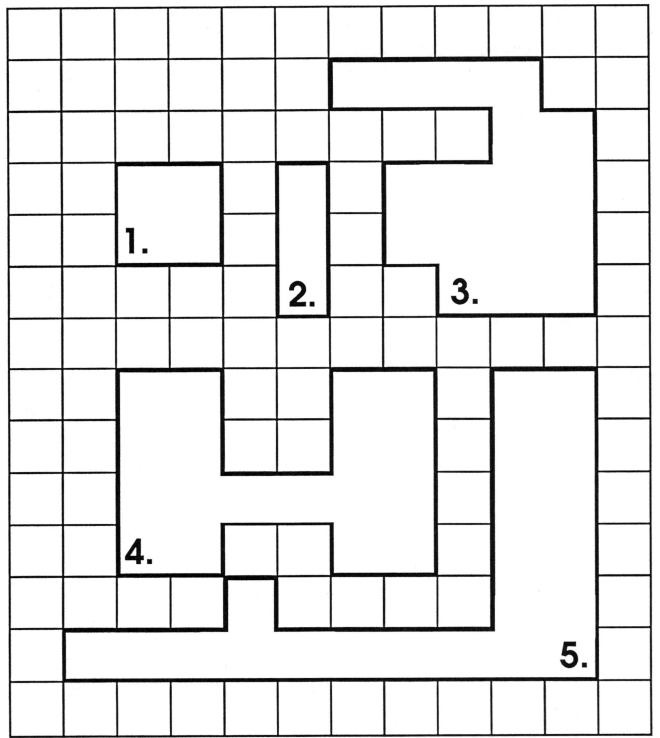

© 1990 by Incentive Publications, Inc., Nashville, TN.

* Answer Key

GEOMETRIC PROBLEMS: TRIANGLES AND RECTANGLES V

How many triangles are missing in each numbered space?
Write the answer in the numbered space.

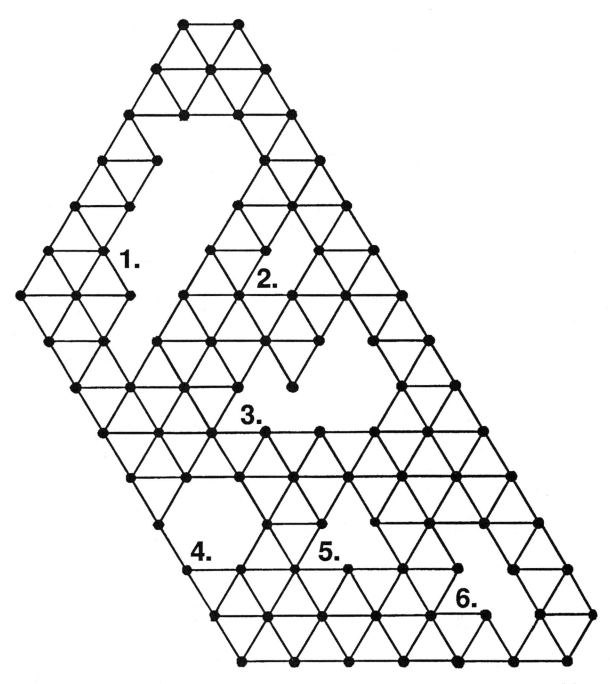

© 1990 by Incentive Publications, Inc., Nashville, TN.
Design from *Geometrical Design Coloring Book* by Spyros Horemis, © 1973 by Dover Publishing, Inc.

* Answer Key

Challenge

GEOMETRIC PROBLEMS:
TRIANGLES AND RECTANGLES VI

How many tiles are missing in each numbered space?
Write the answer in the numbered space.

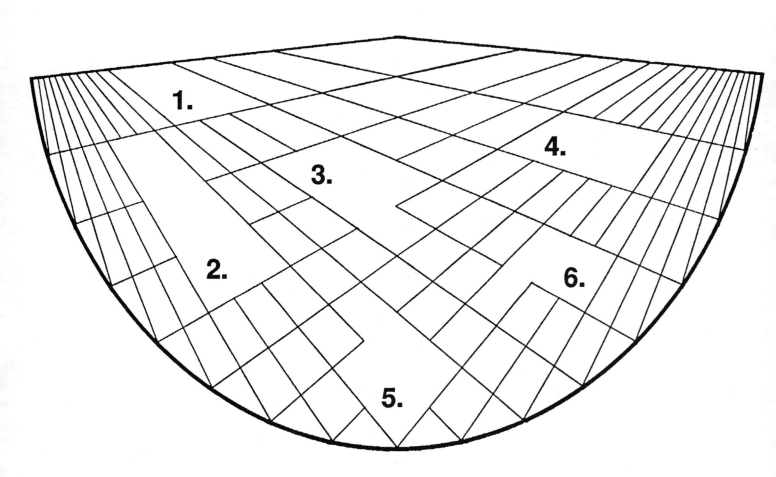

© 1990 by Incentive Publications, Inc., Nashville, TN.
Design from *Geometrical Design Coloring Book* by Spyros Horemis, © 1973 by Dover Publishing, Inc.

* Answer Key

PATTERNS: PATTERN SEARCH

The Problem: Finding the pattern in several series of increasingly complex sets of figures.

The Activity: Reproduce and distribute pages 46-49. Instruct the students to complete the pattern in each row by filling in the blank boxes.

PROCESS/SKILLS CHART

Complex Process
- ✓ **Critical Thinking**
- ✓ **Creative Thinking**

Thought Scheme
- Convergent Thinking
- ✓ **Divergent Thinking**

Content Skills
- Reading Skills Required
- Writing Skills Required
- ✓ **Counting Skills Required**

Basic Skills
- ✓ **Analysis**
- Categorizing
- Classifying
- ✓ **Comparison**

Conditional Logic
- ✓ **Deductive Reasoning**
- Grouping
- Hypothesizing
- Identification
- ✓ **Imagination**
- Inductive Reasoning
- ✓ **Inference**
- Intuition
- Labeling
- ✓ **Logical Reasoning**
- Originality
- ✓ **Part to Whole Relationships**
- ✓ **Patterning**
- Relationships (Visual)
- ✓ **Sequencing**
- ✓ **Spatial Relationships**
- ✓ **Synthesis**
- ✓ **Transformations**

Notes:

Name _____

PATTERNS: PATTERN SEARCH I

Determine the pattern in each row.
Complete the pattern by filling in the empty boxes.
The first one has been done for you.

© 1990 by Incentive Publications, Inc., Nashville, TN.

* Answer Key

PATTERNS: PATTERN SEARCH II

Determine the pattern in each row.
Complete the pattern by filling in the empty boxes.

1.

2.

3.

4.

5.

© 1990 by Incentive Publications, Inc., Nashville, TN.

* Answer Key

PATTERNS: PATTERN SEARCH III

Determine the pattern in each row.
Complete the pattern by filling in the empty boxes.

1.	Ɐ	∀		∀		
2.		◰	◰	◰		
3.				C⇄	⇄C	C⇄
4.	B b	b B			B b	
5.	E e		E e	E		

© 1990 by Incentive Publications, Inc., Nashville, TN.

* Answer Key

Name _____

PATTERNS: PATTERN SEARCH IV

Determine the pattern in each row.
Complete the pattern by filling in the empty boxes.

1.

t t t t	t t t t	t t t t			

2.

| p ■ 222222 | pp ■ 22222 | ppp ■ 2222 | | | |

3.

| ⊥ T | T ⊥ | ⊥ T | | | |

4.

| N U | H U | N U | | | |

5.

| 1 9 | 2 8 | 3 7 | | | |

© 1990 by Incentive Publications, Inc., Nashville, TN.

* Answer Key

49

PATTERNS: LETTER SEARCH

The Problem: Visually discriminating familiar figures in a complex pattern.

The Activity: Reproduce and distribute pages 51 and 52. Instruct the students to find the letter of the alphabet in each pattern, to write it in the box, and to color as many letters in each pattern as they can find.

PROCESS/SKILLS CHART

Complex Process
   Critical Thinking
   ✓ **Creative Thinking**

Thought Scheme
   ✓ **Convergent Thinking**
   Divergent Thinking

Content Skills
   Reading Skills Required
   Writing Skills Required
   Counting Skills Required

Basic Skills
   ✓ **Analysis**
   Categorizing
   Classifying
   Comparison

   Conditional Logic
   ✓ **Deductive Reasoning**
   Grouping
   Hypothesizing
   Identification
   ✓ **Imagination**
   Inductive Reasoning
   ✓ **Inference**
   Intuition
   ✓ **Labeling**
   Logical Reasoning
   Originality
   Part to Whole Relationships
   Patterning
   ✓ **Relationships (Visual)**
   Sequencing
   Spatial Relationships
   Synthesis
   Transformations

Notes:

PATTERNS: LETTER SEARCH I

Find the letter that "makes" each pattern and write it in the box.
Color as many letters as you can find in each pattern.

© 1990 by Incentive Publications, Inc., Nashville, TN.

* Answer Key

PATTERNS: LETTER SEARCH II

Find the letter that "makes" each pattern and write it in the box.
Color as many letters as you can find in each pattern.

© 1990 by Incentive Publications, Inc., Nashville, TN.

* Answer Key

PATTERNS: LETTER MATCH

The Problem: Visually discriminating familiar figures in a complex pattern.

The Activity: Reproduce and distribute pages 54-57. Instruct the students to cut out all of the squares and to match two different patterns for each letter.

Enrichment: Let the students trace bulletin board letter patterns and stencils on construction paper or newsprint to create their own complex alphabet pictures and puzzles.

PROCESS/SKILLS CHART

Complex Process
Critical Thinking
✓ **Creative Thinking**

Thought Scheme
✓ **Convergent Thinking**
Divergent Thinking

Content Skills
Reading Skills Required
Writing Skills Required
Counting Skills Required

Basic Skills
✓ **Analysis**
Categorizing
Classifying
✓ **Comparison**

Conditional Logic
✓ **Deductive Reasoning**
Grouping
Hypothesizing
✓ **Identification**
✓ **Imagination**
Inductive Reasoning
✓ **Inference**
Intuition
Labeling
Logical Reasoning
Originality
✓ **Part to Whole Relationships**
Patterning
Relationships (Visual)
Sequencing
Spatial Relationships
✓ **Synthesis**
Transformations

Notes:

PATTERNS: LETTER MATCH

Cut out the squares on pages 54-57.
Match two different patterns for each letter.

© 1990 by Incentive Publications, Inc., Nashville, TN.

* Answer Key

PATTERNS: LETTER MATCH

© 1990 by Incentive Publications, Inc., Nashville, TN.

PATTERNS: LETTER MATCH

© 1990 by Incentive Publications, Inc., Nashville, TN.

PATTERNS: LETTER MATCH

© 1990 by Incentive Publications, Inc., Nashville, TN.

PUZZLES: ALPHA-MYSTERY

The Problem: Visually reconstructing a shape from scrambled pieces after inferring the desired shape.

The Activity: Reproduce and distribute pages 59-63. Instruct the students to determine the letter in the pattern pieces, to cut out the pieces and to assemble them to form that letter.

PROCESS/SKILLS CHART

Complex Process
Critical Thinking
✓ **Creative Thinking**

Thought Scheme
✓ **Convergent Thinking**
Divergent Thinking

Content Skills
Reading Skills Required
Writing Skills Required
Counting Skills Required

Basic Skills
✓ **Analysis**
Categorizing
Classifying
✓ **Comparison**

Conditional Logic
✓ **Deductive Reasoning**
Grouping
Hypothesizing
✓ **Identification**
Imagination
Inductive Reasoning
✓ **Inference**
Intuition
Labeling
Logical Reasoning
Originality
✓ **Part to Whole Relationships**
Patterning
Relationships (Visual)
Sequencing
✓ **Spatial Relationships**
Synthesis
Transformations

Notes:

PUZZLES: ALPHA-MYSTERY I

Determine what letter is in the pattern pieces below.
Color at least one letter.
Cut out the pattern pieces and assemble them to form the letter.

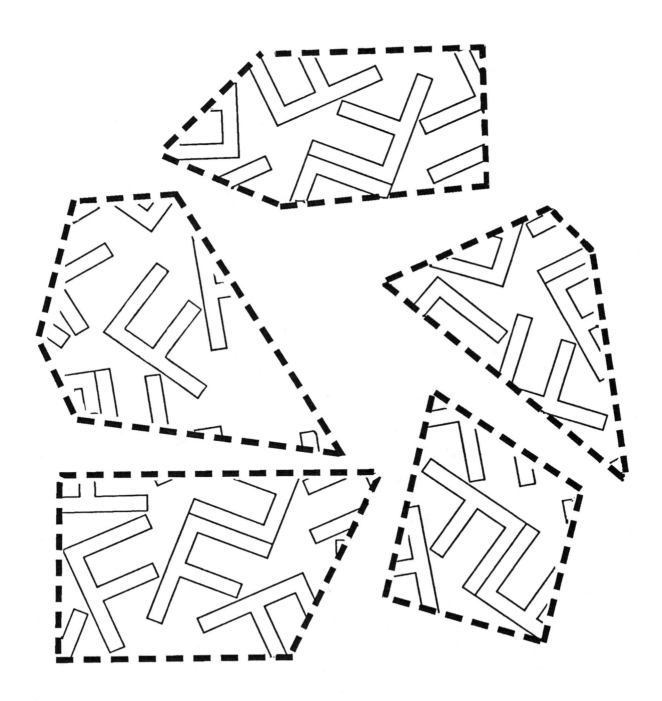

© 1990 by Incentive Publications, Inc., Nashville, TN.

* Answer Key

PUZZLES: ALPHA-MYSTERY II

Determine what letter is in the pattern pieces below.
Color at least one letter.
Cut out the pattern pieces and assemble them to form the letter.

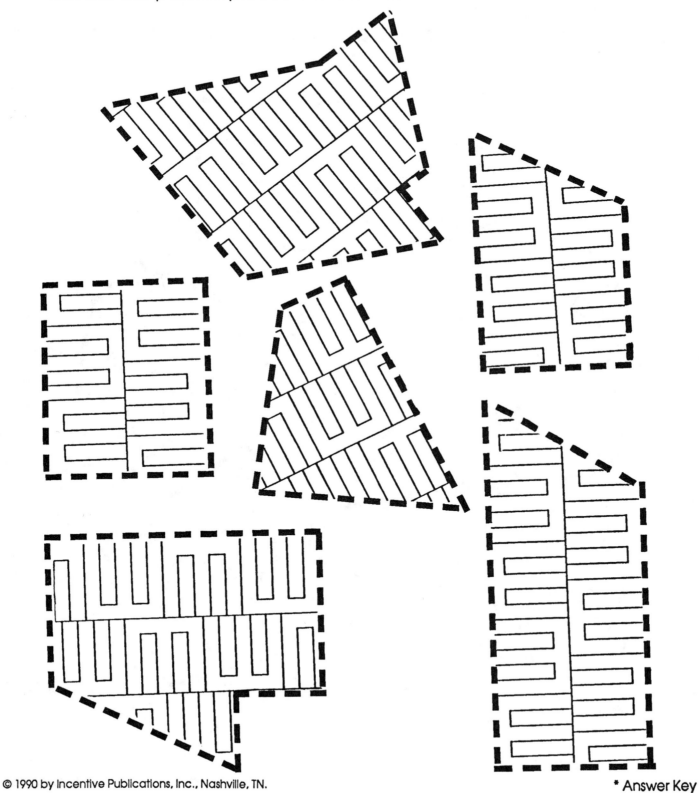

© 1990 by Incentive Publications, Inc., Nashville, TN.

* Answer Key

PUZZLES: ALPHA-MYSTERY III

Determine what letter is in the pattern pieces below.
Color at least one letter.
Cut out the pattern pieces and assemble them to form the letter.

© 1990 by Incentive Publications, Inc., Nashville, TN.

* Answer Key

PUZZLES: ALPHA-MYSTERY IV

Determine what letter is in the pattern pieces below.
Color at least one letter.
Cut out the pattern pieces and assemble them to form the letter.

© 1990 by Incentive Publications, Inc., Nashville, TN.

* Answer Key

PUZZLES: ALPHA-MYSTERY V

Determine what letter is in the pattern pieces below.
Color at least one letter.
Cut out the pattern pieces and assemble them to form the letter.

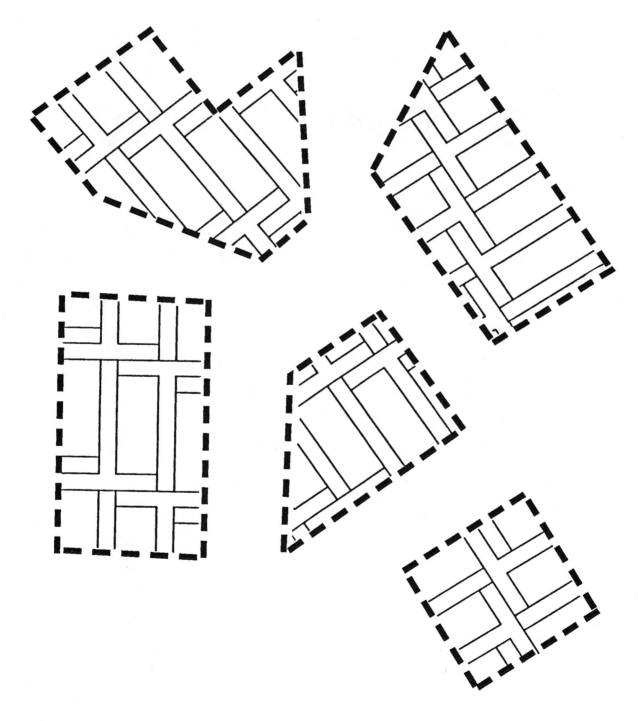

© 1990 by Incentive Publications, Inc., Nashville, TN.

* Answer Key

PUZZLES: ALPHA-MYSTERY
DOUBLE TROUBLE

The Problem: Visually discriminating and grouping two different patterns and then reconstructing the shapes from scrambled pieces.

The Activity: Reproduce and distribute pages 65 and 66. Instruct the students to cut out the pattern pieces, to group the two different patterns and to assemble the pieces to form those letters.

PROCESS/SKILLS CHART

Complex Process
  Critical Thinking
  ✓ **Creative Thinking**

Thought Scheme
  ✓ **Convergent Thinking**
  Divergent Thinking

Content Skills
  Reading Skills Required
  Writing Skills Required
  Counting Skills Required

Basic Skills
  ✓ **Analysis**
  ✓ **Categorizing**
  Classifying
  ✓ **Comparison**

Conditional Logic
✓ **Deductive Reasoning**
✓ **Grouping**
  Hypothesizing
✓ **Identification**
✓ **Imagination**
  Inductive Reasoning
✓ **Inference**
  Intuition
  Labeling
  Logical Reasoning
  Originality
✓ **Part to Whole Relationships**
  Patterning
✓ **Relationships (Visual)**
  Sequencing
✓ **Spatial Relationships**
  Synthesis
  Transformations

Notes:

PUZZLES: ALPHA-MYSTERY
DOUBLE TROUBLE I

Determine what two letters are in the pattern pieces below.
Color at least one of each letter.
Cut out the pattern pieces and assemble them to form two letters.

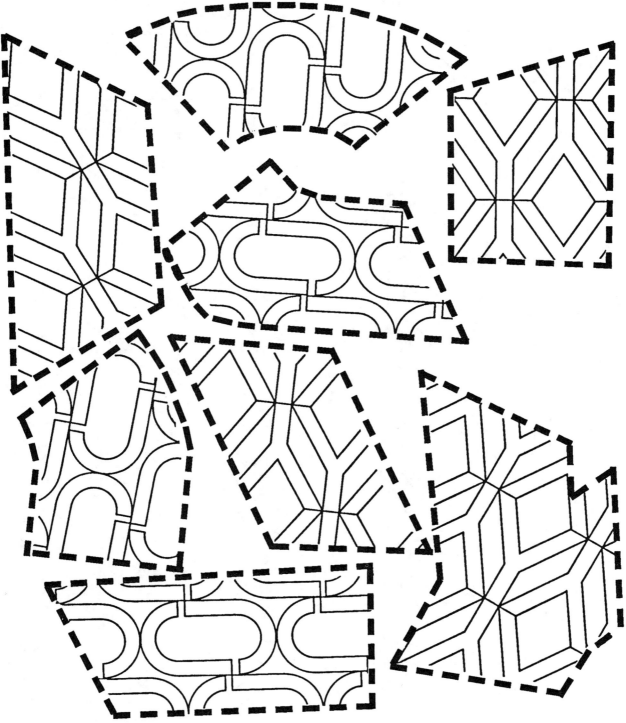

© 1990 by Incentive Publications, Inc., Nashville, TN.

* Answer Key

PUZZLES: ALPHA-MYSTERY DOUBLE TROUBLE II

Determine what two letters are in the pattern pieces below.
Color at least one of each letter.
Cut out the pattern pieces and assemble them to form two letters.

© 1990 by Incentive Publications, Inc., Nashville TN

* Answer Key

DESTINATION-CLASSIFICATION: TWO GROUPS

The Problem: Discriminating between two sets of related figures and grouping them.

The Activity: Reproduce and distribute pages 68-71. Instruct the students to find the figures that are alike and to draw them in the boxes under the correct category heading.

PROCESS/SKILLS CHART

Complex Process
- ✓ Critical Thinking
- ✓ Creative Thinking

Thought Scheme
- Convergent Thinking
- ✓ Divergent Thinking

Content Skills
- Reading Skills Required
- Writing Skills Required
- Counting Skills Required

Basic Skills
- ✓ Analysis
- ✓ Categorizing
- Classifying
- ✓ Comparison

- Conditional Logic
- Deductive Reasoning
- ✓ Grouping
- ✓ Hypothesizing
- ✓ Identification
- Imagination
- ✓ Inductive Reasoning
- ✓ Inference
- Intuition
- Labeling
- Logical Reasoning
- Originality
- Part to Whole Relationships
- Patterning
- ✓ Relationships (Visual)
- Sequencing
- Spatial Relationships
- ✓ Synthesis
- ✓ Transformations

Notes:

67

DESTINATION-CLASSIFICATION: TWO GROUPS I

Find the figures that are alike and draw them in the boxes under the correct category heading.
The first one has been done for you.

1.

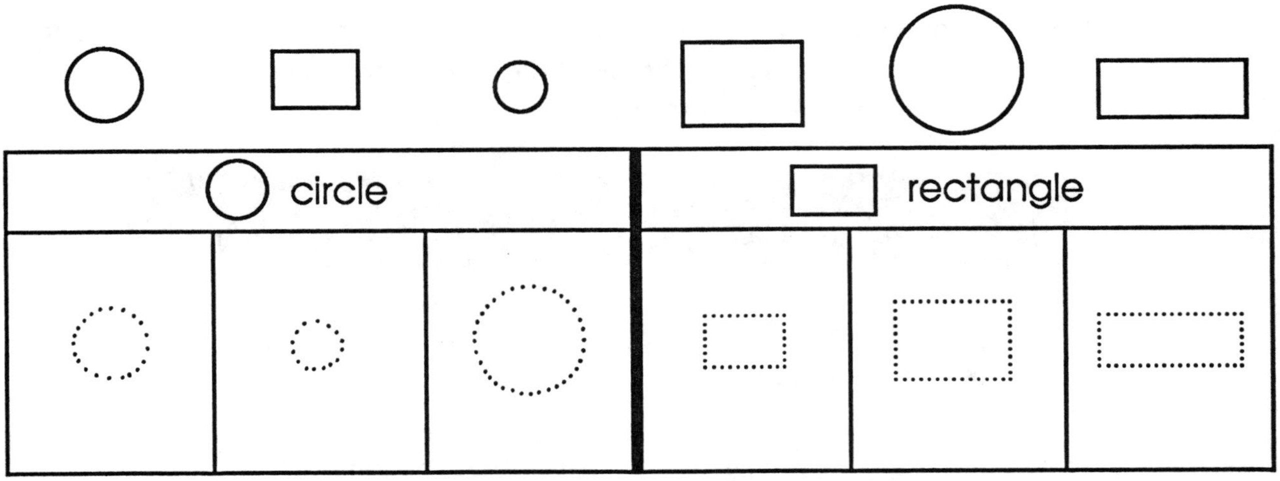

◯ circle			▭ rectangle		

2.

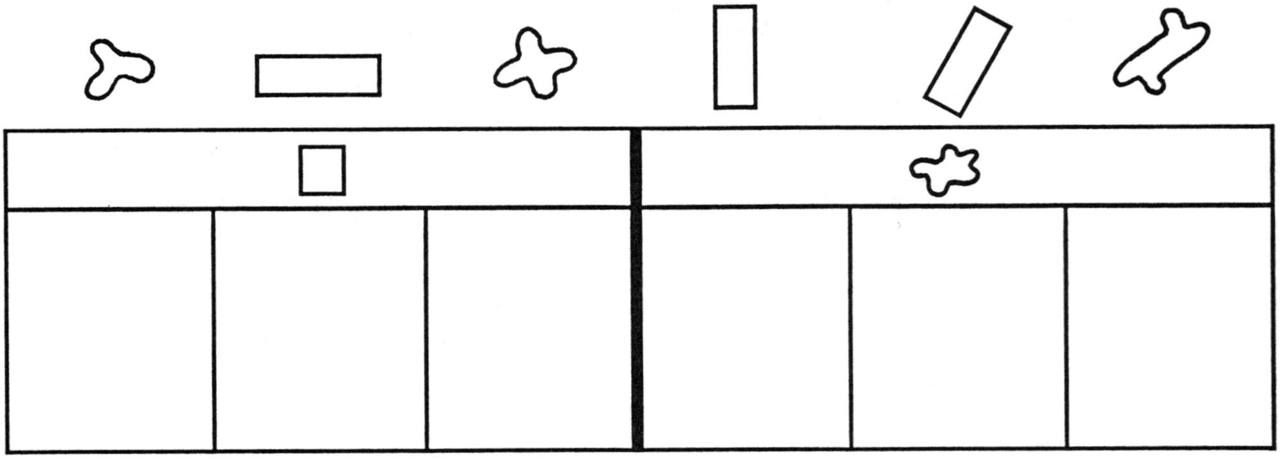

□			✿		

3.

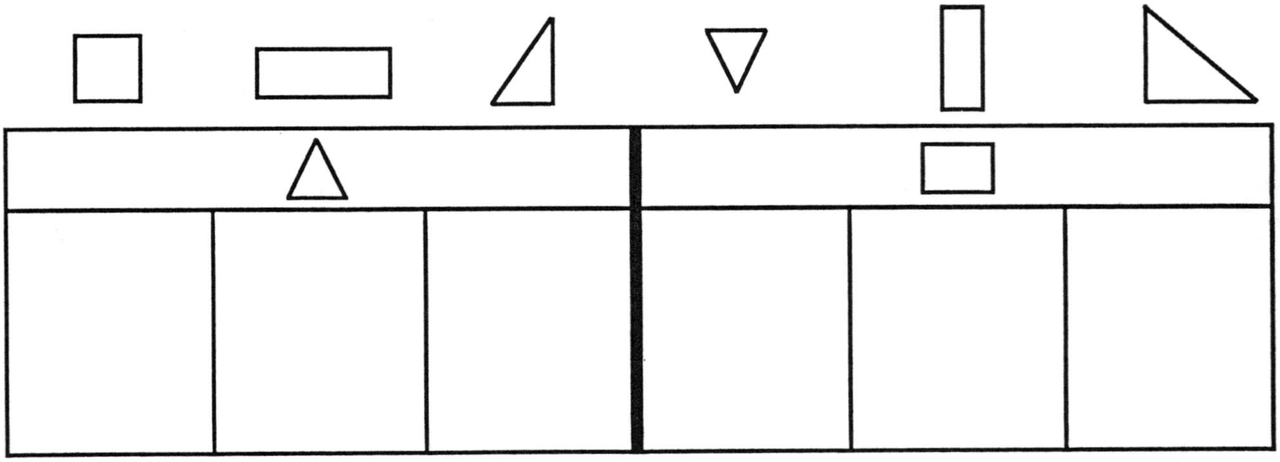

△			▭		

© 1990 by Incentive Publications, Inc., Nashville, TN.

* Answer Key

Name _____

DESTINATION-CLASSIFICATION: TWO GROUPS II

Find the figures that are alike and draw them in the boxes under the correct category heading.

T   8   U   5   6   W

1.

	7			Y	

(arrows)

2.

	⬅			↗	

O   T   E   Q   D   F

3.

	8			7	

© 1990 by Incentive Publications, Inc., Nashville, TN.

* Answer Key

DESTINATION-CLASSIFICATION: TWO GROUPS III

Find the figures that are alike and draw them in the boxes under the correct category heading.

N   **U**   X   M   E   **H**

1.

S			R		

e   **p**   **D**   **A**   i   L

2.

W			k		

3.

© 1990 by Incentive Publications, Inc., Nashville, TN.

* Answer Key

DESTINATION-CLASSIFICATION: TWO GROUPS IV

Find the figures that are alike and draw them in the boxes under the correct category heading.

1.

2.

3.

© 1990 by Incentive Publications, Inc., Nashville, TN.

* Answer Key

DESTINATION-CLASSIFICATION: YOU MAKE THE THIRD ONE

The Problem: Discriminating between two sets of related figures, grouping them, and drawing an original related figure for each category.

The Activity: Reproduce and distribute pages 73 and 74. Instruct the students to find the figures that are alike, to draw them in the boxes under the correct category heading, and to draw a third related figure to complete each group.

PROCESS/SKILLS CHART

Complex Process
- ✓ Critical Thinking
- ✓ Creative Thinking

Thought Scheme
- Convergent Thinking
- ✓ Divergent Thinking

Content Skills
- Reading Skills Required
- Writing Skills Required
- Counting Skills Required

Basic Skills
- ✓ Analysis
- ✓ Categorizing
- ✓ Classifying
- ✓ Comparison

- Conditional Logic
- Deductive Reasoning
- ✓ Grouping
- Hypothesizing
- ✓ Identification
- Imagination
- ✓ Inductive Reasoning
- ✓ Inference
- Intuition
- Labeling
- Logical Reasoning
- ✓ Originality
- ✓ Part to Whole Relationships
- Patterning
- ✓ Relationships (Visual)
- Sequencing
- Spatial Relationships
- ✓ Synthesis
- Transformations

Notes:

Name _____

DESTINATION-CLASSIFICATION:
YOU MAKE THE THIRD ONE I

Find the figures that are alike and draw them in the boxes under
the correct category heading.
Then draw a third related figure to complete each group.
The first one has been done for you.

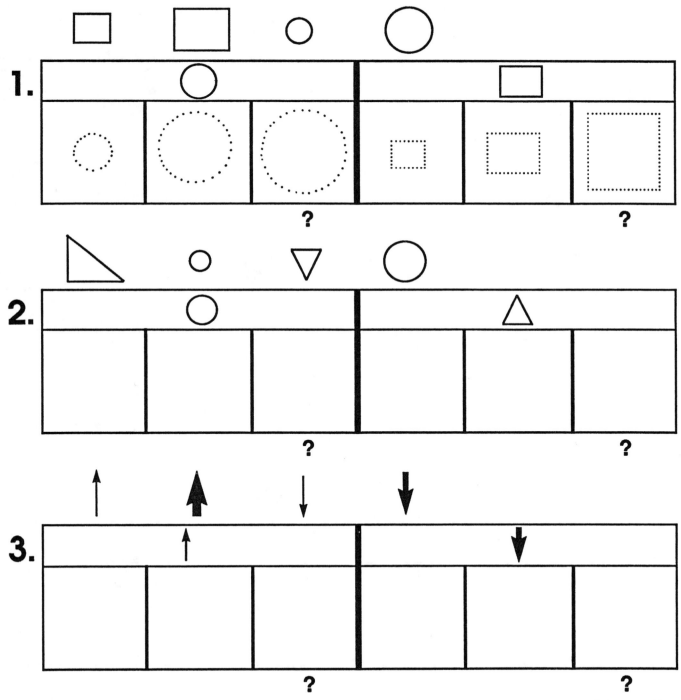

© 1990 by Incentive Publications, Inc., Nashville, TN.

* Answer Key

Name _____

DESTINATION-CLASSIFICATION: YOU MAKE THE THIRD ONE II

Find the figures that are alike and draw them in the boxes under the correct category heading.
Then draw a third related figure to complete each group.

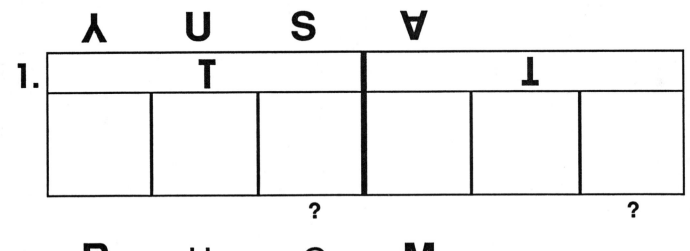

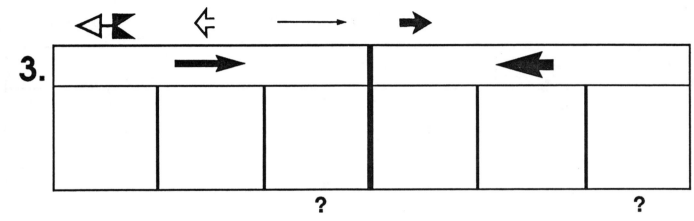

* Answer Key

IDENTIFY/CLASSIFY:
YOU DECIDE THE DIFFERENCE

The Problem: Discriminating between two sets of related figures and grouping them without the benefit of category headings.

The Activity: Reproduce and distribute pages 76-78. Instruct the students to find the figures that are alike and to group them in the boxes.

PROCESS/SKILLS CHART

Complex Process
- ✓ **Critical Thinking**
- Creative Thinking

Thought Scheme
- ✓ **Convergent Thinking**
- Divergent Thinking

Content Skills
- Reading Skills Required
- Writing Skills Required
- Counting Skills Required

Basic Skills
- ✓ **Analysis**
- ✓ **Categorizing**
- ✓ **Classifying**
- ✓ **Comparison**

- Conditional Logic
- Deductive Reasoning
- ✓ **Grouping**
- ✓ **Hypothesizing**
- ✓ **Identification**
- Imagination
- ✓ **Inductive Reasoning**
- ✓ **Inference**
- Intuition
- Labeling
- Logical Reasoning
- Originality
- ✓ **Part to Whole Relationships**
- Patterning
- ✓ **Relationships (Visual)**
- Sequencing
- Spatial Relationships
- ✓ **Synthesis**
- Transformations

Notes:

Name _____

IDENTIFY/CLASSIFY:
YOU DECIDE THE DIFFERENCE I

Find the figures that are alike and group them in the boxes provided.
The first one has been done for you.

1.

2.

3.

IDENTIFY/CLASSIFY:
YOU DECIDE THE DIFFERENCE II

Find the figures that are alike and group them in the boxes provided.

1.

2.

3.

© 1990 by Incentive Publications, Inc., Nashville, TN.

* Answer Key

Name _____

IDENTIFY/CLASSIFY:
YOU DECIDE THE DIFFERENCE III

Find the figures that are alike and group them in the boxes provided.

1.

2.

3.

© 1990 by Incentive Publications, Inc., Nashville, TN.

* Answer Key

IDENTIFY/CLASSIFY: FOUR CATEGORIES

The Problem: Finding two different ways to group the same six figures.

The Activity: Reproduce and distribute pages 80-83. Instruct the students to do the following:

1. Find the most obvious way to group the six figures into two groups and draw them accordingly in the first row of boxes.

2. Regroup the same six figures according to a different "likeness/difference" relationship and draw them accordingly in the second row of boxes.

PROCESS/SKILLS CHART

Complex Process
- ✓ **Critical Thinking**
- Creative Thinking

Thought Scheme
- Convergent Thinking
- ✓ **Divergent Thinking**

Content Skills
- Reading Skills Required
- Writing Skills Required
- Counting Skills Required

Basic Skills
- ✓ **Analysis**
- ✓ **Categorizing**
- ✓ **Classifying**
- ✓ **Comparison**

Conditional Logic
Deductive Reasoning
- ✓ **Grouping**
- ✓ **Hypothesizing**
- ✓ **Identification**
Imagination
Inductive Reasoning
- ✓ **Inference**
Intuition
Labeling
- ✓ **Logical Reasoning**
Originality
- ✓ **Part to Whole Relationships**
Patterning
- ✓ **Relationships (Visual)**
Sequencing
Spatial Relationships
- ✓ **Synthesis**
Transformations

Notes:

IDENTIFY/CLASSIFY: FOUR CATEGORIES I

Find the most obvious way to group the six figures into two groups and draw them accordingly in the first row of boxes.

Regroup the same six figures according to a different "likeness/ difference" relationship and draw them accordingly in the second row of boxes.

The first one has been done for you.

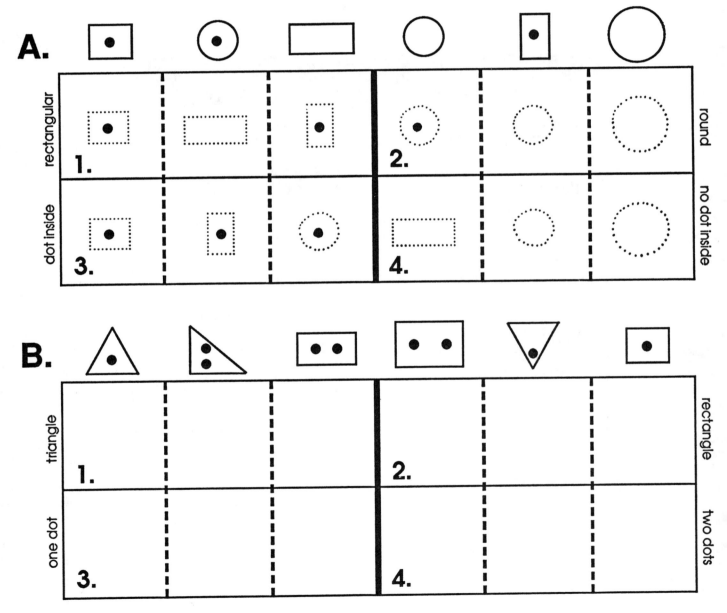

© 1990 by Incentive Publications, Inc., Nashville, TN.

* Answer Key

Name _____

IDENTIFY/CLASSIFY: FOUR CATEGORIES II

Find the most obvious way to group the six figures into two groups and draw them accordingly in the first row of boxes.

Regroup the same six figures according to a different "likeness/ difference" relationship and draw them accordingly in the second row of boxes.

Each has been partially done for you.

A.

1.			2.		
3.			4.		

B.

1.			2.		
3.			4.		

© 1990 by Incentive Publications, Inc., Nashville, TN.

* Answer Key

IDENTIFY/CLASSIFY: FOUR CATEGORIES III

Find the most obvious way to group the six figures into two groups and draw them accordingly in the first row of boxes.

Regroup the same six figures according to a different "likeness/difference" relationship and draw them accordingly in the second row of boxes.

A. ← ⇦ ⬌ ← ↔ ⬌

1.			2.		
3.			4.		

B. R   T   r   m   M   †

1.			2.		
3.			4.		

© 1990 by Incentive Publications, Inc., Nashville, TN.

* Answer Key

IDENTIFY/CLASSIFY: FOUR CATEGORIES IV

Find the most obvious way to group the six figures into two groups and draw them accordingly in the first row of boxes.

Regroup the same six figures according to a different "likeness/difference" relationship and draw them accordingly in the second row of boxes.

A.

1.			2.		
3.			4.		

B.

1.			2.		
3.			4.		

© 1990 by Incentive Publications, Inc., Nashville, TN.

* Answer Key

IDENTIFY/CLASSIFY:
SIX CATEGORIES

The Problem: Finding three different ways to group the same six figures.

The Activity: Reproduce and distribute pages 85-87. Instruct the students to do the following:

1. Find the most obvious way to group the six figures into two groups and draw them accordingly in the first row of boxes.

2. Regroup the six figures according to a different "likeness/difference" relationship and draw them accordingly in the second row of boxes.

3. Regroup the same six figures according to a third set of criteria and draw them accordingly in the third row of boxes.

Note: This is a *very difficult* activity! Try it yourself before presenting it to the students.

PROCESS/SKILLS CHART

Complex Process
- ✓ Critical Thinking
- ✓ Creative Thinking

Thought Scheme
- Convergent Thinking
- ✓ Divergent Thinking

Content Skills
- Reading Skills Required
- Writing Skills Required
- Counting Skills Required

Basic Skills
- ✓ Analysis
- ✓ Categorizing
- ✓ Classifying
- ✓ Comparison

Conditional Logic
Deductive Reasoning
- ✓ Grouping
- ✓ Hypothesizing
- ✓ Identification
Imagination
- ✓ Inductive Reasoning
Inference
Intuition
Labeling
- ✓ Logical Reasoning
Originality
- ✓ Part to Whole Relationships
Patterning
- ✓ Relationships (Visual)
Sequencing
- ✓ Spatial Relationships
- ✓ Synthesis
Transformations

Notes:

Name _____

IDENTIFY/CLASSIFY: SIX CATEGORIES I

Group the six figures according to six different categories by completing the chart below.

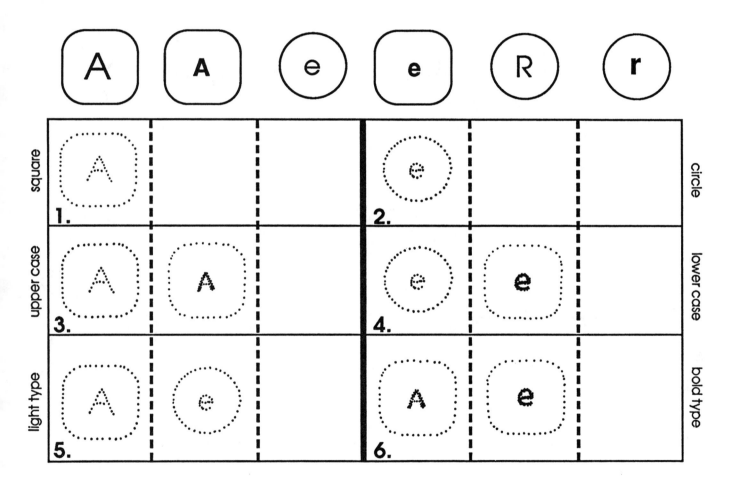

© 1990 by Incentive Publications, Inc., Nashville, TN.

* Answer Key

IDENTIFY/CLASSIFY: SIX CATEGORIES II

Group the six figures according to six different categories by completing the chart below.

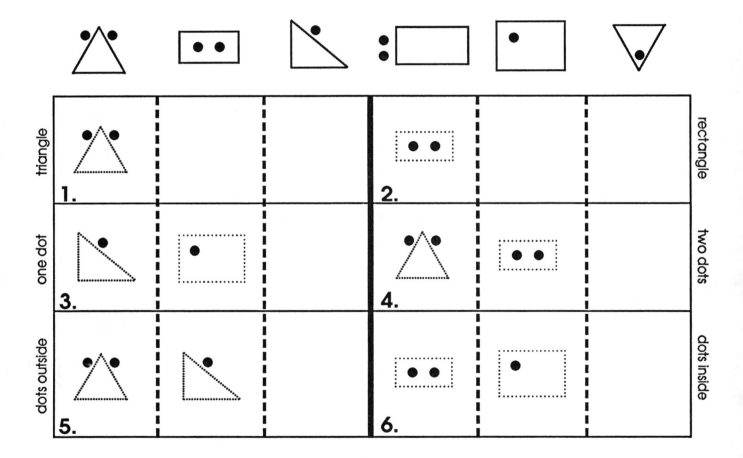

© 1990 by Incentive Publications, Inc., Nashville, TN.

* Answer Key

 # IDENTIFY/CLASSIFY: SIX CATEGORIES III

Find the most obvious way to group the six figures into two groups and draw them accordingly in the first row of boxes.

Regroup the six figures according to a different "likeness/difference" relationship and draw them accordingly in the second row of boxes.

Regroup the six figures again according to a third "likeness/difference" relationship and draw them accordingly in the third row of boxes.

Label each group.

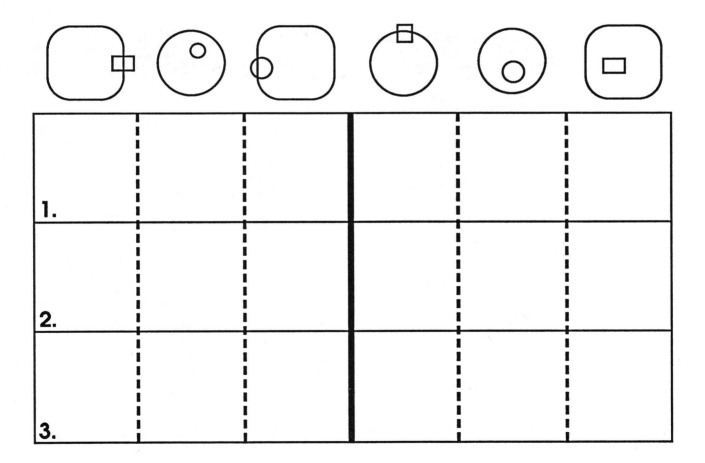

© 1990 by Incentive Publications, Inc., Nashville, TN.

* Answer Key

IDENTIFY/CLASSIFY: VENN DIAGRAMS

The Problem: Noting the relationships of a set of figures and classifying them on a Venn diagram.

The Activity: Reproduce and distribute pages 89-97. Instruct the students to separate the figures into three groups. The two outside groups should be completely different and the inside group should be a set of figures related to both outside groups. Students should draw or glue (according to the activity) the figures in the correct area of the Venn diagram.

Enrichment: Have the students create original figures to fit into each group.

Draw a Venn diagram on a large piece of paper and have the students cut out magazine pictures that can be grouped on the diagram (color relationships, activity relationships, word or story relationships, etc.).

PROCESS/SKILLS CHART

Complex Process
- ✓ Critical Thinking
- ✓ Creative Thinking

Thought Scheme
- Convergent Thinking
- ✓ Divergent Thinking

Content Skills
- Reading Skills Required
- Writing Skills Required
- Counting Skills Required

Basic Skills
- ✓ Analysis
- ✓ Categorizing
- ✓ Classifying
- ✓ Comparison

Conditional Logic
Deductive Reasoning
- ✓ Grouping
- ✓ Hypothesizing
- ✓ Identification
- Imagination
- ✓ Inductive Reasoning
- ✓ Inference
- Intuition
- ✓ Labeling
- ✓ Logical Reasoning
- Originality
- ✓ Part to Whole Relationships
- Patterning
- ✓ Relationships (Visual)
- Sequencing
- ✓ Spatial Relationships
- ✓ Synthesis
- ✓ Transformations

Notes:

IDENTIFY/CLASSIFY:
VENN DIAGRAMS I

The six figures in group A have been separated into three groups.
The two outside groups are completely different and the inside group is
related to both outside groups.
Draw the six figures in group B in the correct areas below.

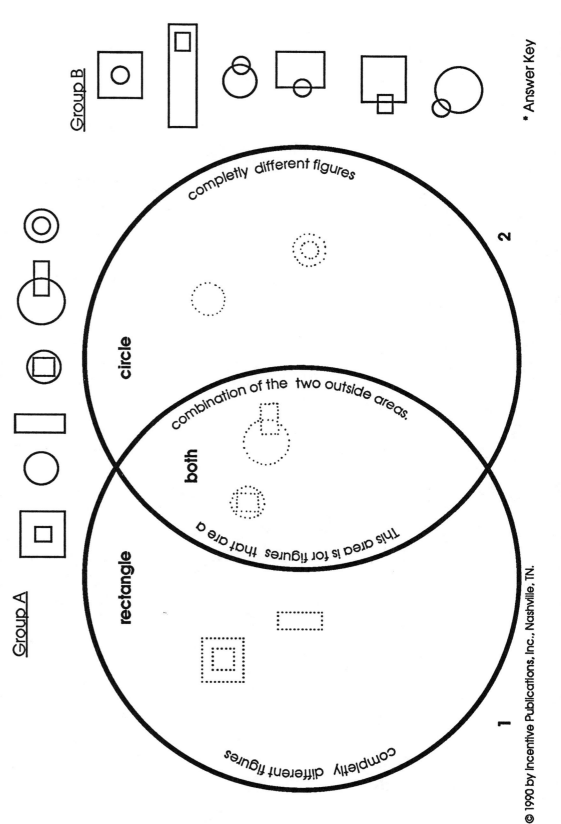

Group A

Group B

circle

completly different figures

combination of the two outside areas.

both

This area is for figures that are a

rectangle

completly different figures

1

2

* Answer Key

© 1990 by Incentive Publications, Inc., Nashville, TN.

IDENTIFY/CLASSIFY:
VENN DIAGRAMS II

The letters in group A have been separated into three groups.
The two outside groups are completely different and the inside group is
related to both outside groups.
Write the letters in group B in the correct areas below.

Group A   KK   kk   Kk

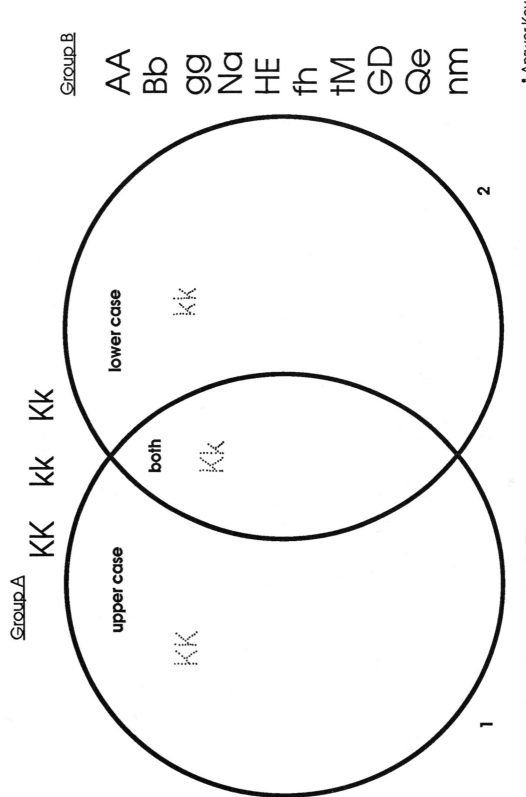

Group B

AA
Bb
gg
Na
HE
fh
tM
GD
Qe
nm

* Answer Key

© 1990 by Incentive Publications, Inc., Nashville, TN.

IDENTIFY/CLASSIFY:
VENN DIAGRAMS III

Separate the characters below into three groups.
The two outside groups should be completely different and the inside group
should be related to both outside groups.
Write the characters in the correct areas and label each category.

34
4s
st
nf
a3
25
Tga
f5t
456
Xr8
pqr
wx9

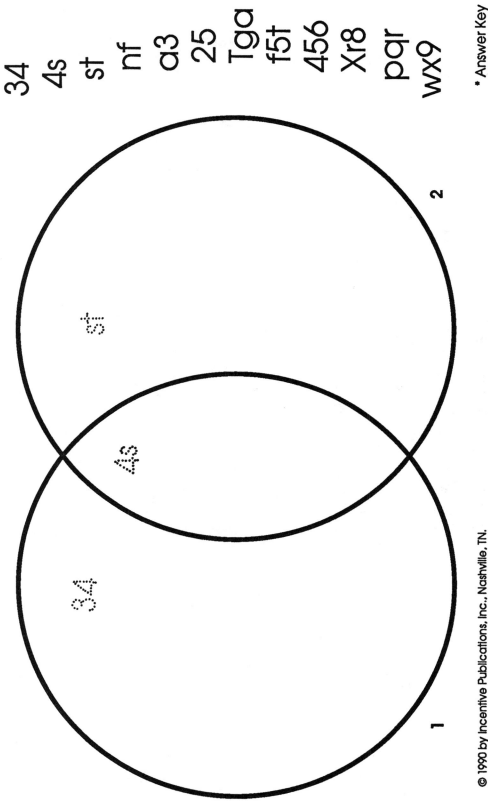

© 1990 by Incentive Publications, Inc., Nashville, TN.

* Answer Key

Name _____

IDENTIFY/CLASSIFY:
VENN DIAGRAMS IV

Separate the figures below into three groups.
The two outside groups should be completely different and the inside group
should be related to both outside groups.
Draw the figures in the correct areas and label each category.

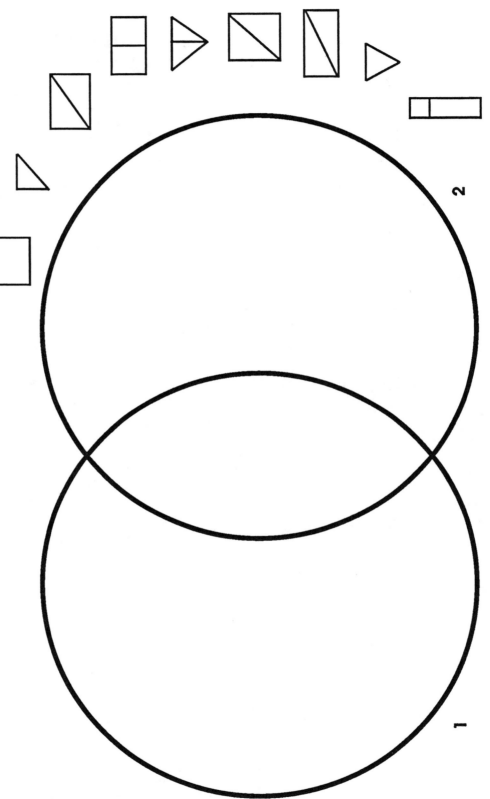

© 1990 by Incentive Publications, Inc., Nashville, TN.

* Answer Key

IDENTIFY/CLASSIFY:
VENN DIAGRAMS V

Separate the figures below into three groups.
The two outside groups should be completely different and the inside group
should be related to both outside groups.
Draw the figures in the correct areas and label each category.

* Answer Key

2

© 1990 by Incentive Publications, Inc., Nashville, TN.

Cut out the figures below.
Separate the figures into three groups.
Glue the figures in the correct areas on page 95 and label each
    category.

Remember: The two outside groups should be completely different
    and the inside group should be related to both outside groups.

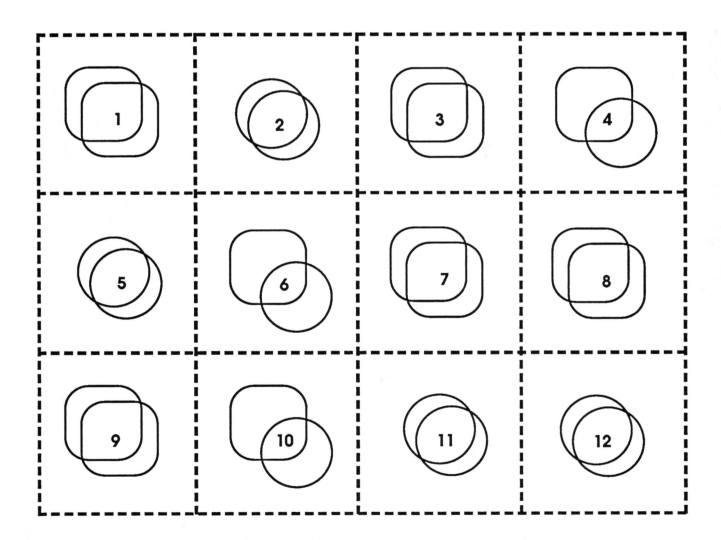

© 1990 by Incentive Publications, Inc., Nashville, TN.

IDENTIFY/CLASSIFY:
VENN DIAGRAMS VI

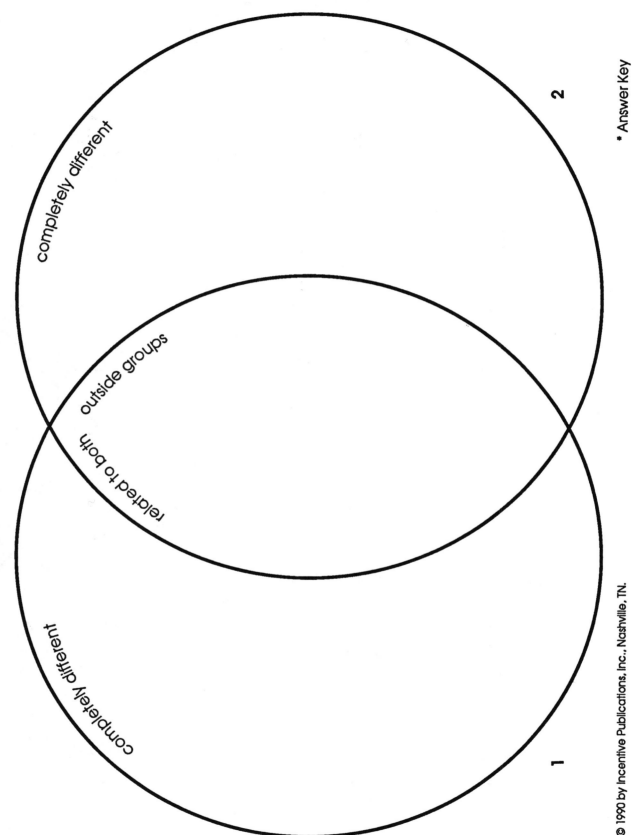

completely different

outside groups

related to both

completely different

2

1

© 1990 by Incentive Publications, Inc., Nashville, TN.

* Answer Key

IDENTIFY/CLASSIFY: VENN DIAGRAMS VII

Cut out the figures below.
Separate the figures into three groups.
Glue the figures in the correct areas on page 97 and
   label each category.

Remember: The two outside groups should be
   completely different and the inside group should be
   related to both outside groups.

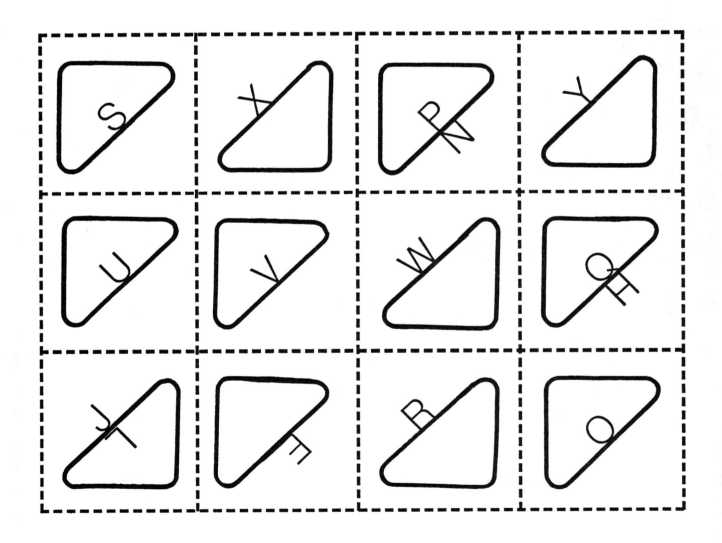

© 1990 by Incentive Publications, Inc., Nashville, TN.

IDENTIFY/CLASSIFY:
VENN DIAGRAMS VII

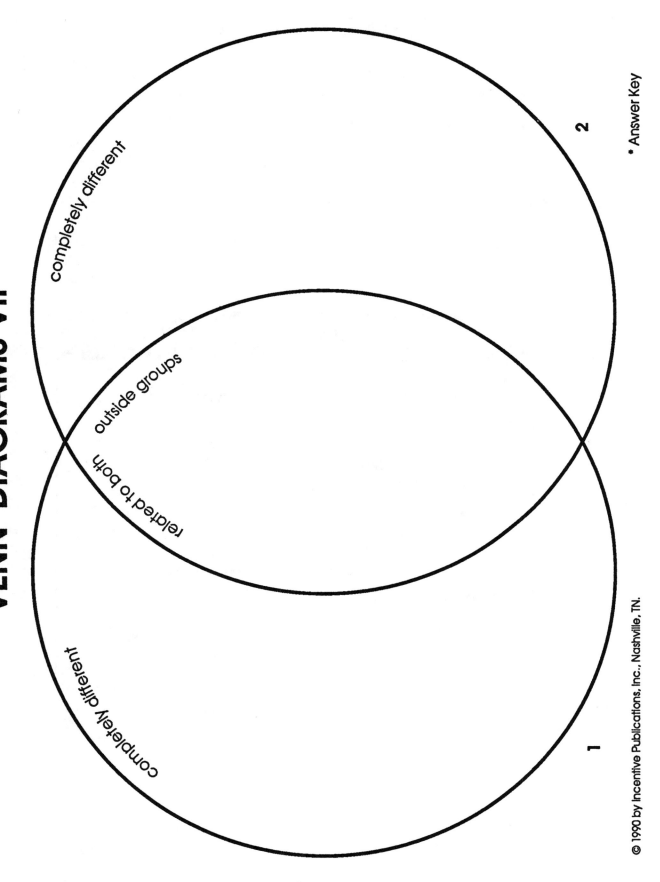

completely different

outside groups

related to both

completely different

2

1

* Answer Key

© 1990 by Incentive Publications, Inc., Nashville, TN.

COMPUTER GEOMETRICS: HIGH-TECH PIE PUZZLES

The Problem: Discriminating between two complex patterns, grouping them and then reconstructing the pattern using visual clues.

The Activity: Reproduce and distribute pages 99-102. Instruct the students to cut out the pie puzzle pieces, separate them into two groups, reassemble the patterns, and glue the pieces in the correct pies.

Enrichment: You or your students can make a variety of puzzles using wallpaper samples. Mix two or three patterns to include grouping in this inference-based activity. (Using wallpaper samples also adds the dimension of color!)

PROCESS/SKILLS CHART

Complex Process
- ✓ **Critical Thinking**
- Creative Thinking

Thought Scheme
- ✓ **Convergent Thinking**
- Divergent Thinking

Content Skills
- Reading Skills Required
- Writing Skills Required
- Counting Skills Required

Basic Skills
- ✓ **Analysis**
- ✓ **Categorizing**
- Classifying
- ✓ **Comparison**

Conditional Logic
- ✓ **Deductive Reasoning**
- ✓ **Grouping**
- Hypothesizing
- ✓ **Identification**
- ✓ **Imagination**
- Inductive Reasoning
- ✓ **Inference**
- Intuition
- Labeling
- Logical Reasoning
- Originality
- ✓ **Part to Whole Relationships**
- ✓ **Patterning**
- ✓ **Relationships (Visual)**
- Sequencing
- ✓ **Spatial Relationships**
- ✓ **Synthesis**
- ✓ **Transformations**

Notes:

COMPUTER GEOMETRICS:
HIGH-TECH PIE PUZZLES I

Cut out the pie puzzle pieces on page 100 and separate them into two groups. Reassemble the patterns and glue the pieces in the correct pies.

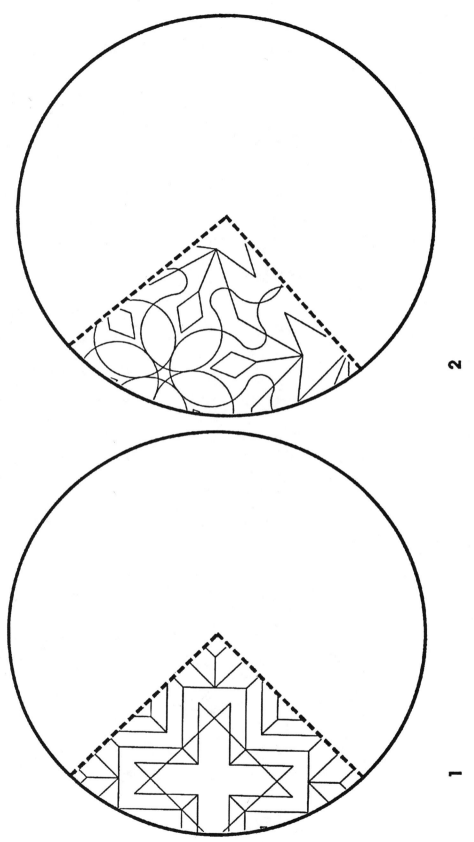

1

2

* Answer Key

© 1990 by Incentive Publications, Inc., Nashville, TN.
Designs from *Computer Geometric Art* by Ian O. Angell, © 1985 by Dover Publications, Inc.

COMPUTER GEOMETRICS:
HIGH-TECH PIE PUZZLES I

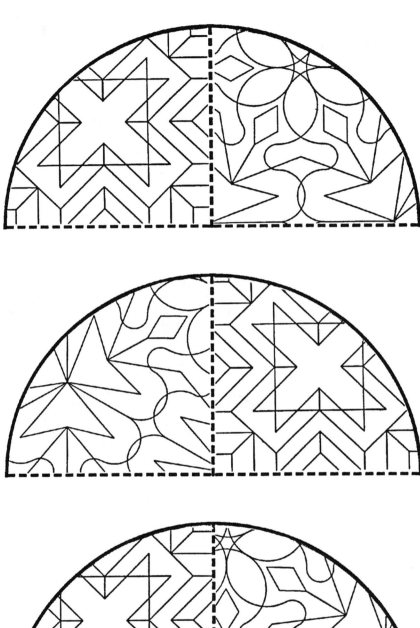

© 1990 by Incentive Publications, Inc., Nashville, TN.
Designs from *Computer Geometric Art* by Ian O. Angell, © 1985 by Dover Publications, Inc.

COMPUTER GEOMETRICS:
HIGH-TECH PIE PUZZLES II

Cut out the pie puzzle pieces on page 102 and separate them into two groups.
Reassemble the patterns and glue the pieces in the correct pies.

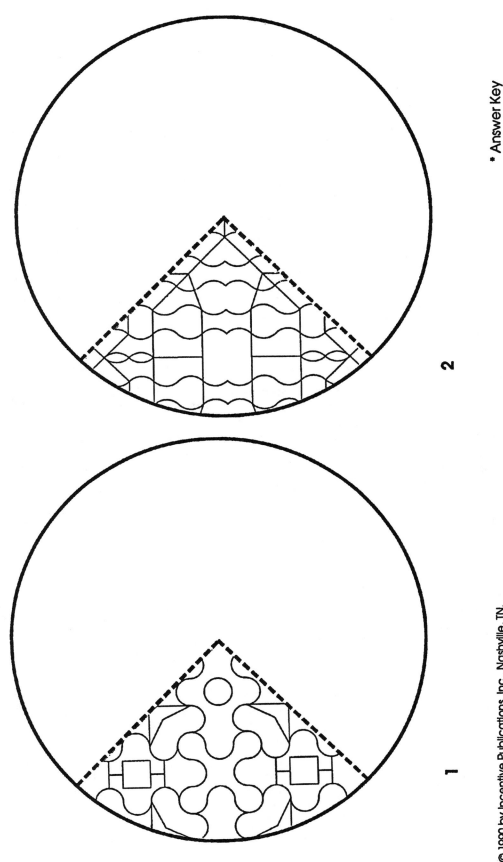

2

1

* Answer Key

© 1990 by Incentive Publications, Inc., Nashville, TN.
Designs from *Computer Geometric Art* by Ian O. Angell, © 1985 by Dover Publications, Inc.

COMPUTER GEOMETRICS:
HIGH-TECH PIE PUZZLES II

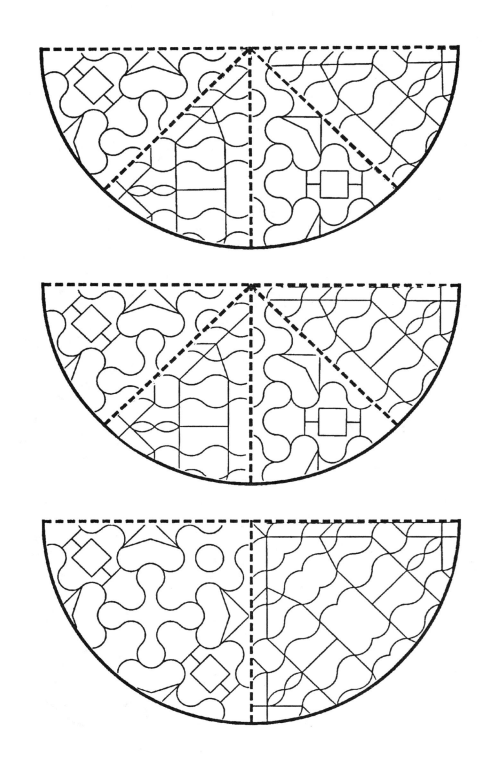

© 1990 by Incentive Publications, Inc., Nashville, TN.
Designs from *Computer Geometric Art* by Ian O. Angell, © 1985 by Dover Publications, Inc.

CREATURE FEATURES

The Problem: Noting the difference/likeness between three sets of figures and using those categories to label additional figures and to create original related figures.

The Activity: Reproduce and distribute pages 104-107. Each set of figures in these activities has been given a nonsense name. Instruct the students to circle the examples of each group according to the directions and to draw an additional related figure for each category at the bottom of the page.

PROCESS/SKILLS CHART

Complex Process
- ✓ **Critical Thinking**
- ✓ **Creative Thinking**

Thought Scheme
- Convergent Thinking
- ✓ **Divergent Thinking**

Content Skills
- Reading Skills Required
- Writing Skills Required
- Counting Skills Required

Basic Skills
- ✓ **Analysis**
- ✓ **Categorizing**
- ✓ **Classifying**
- ✓ **Comparison**

Conditional Logic
- ✓ **Deductive Reasoning**
- ✓ **Grouping**
- ✓ **Hypothesizing**
- ✓ **Identification**
- ✓ **Imagination**
- Inductive Reasoning
- ✓ **Inference**
- Intuition
- ✓ **Labeling**
- ✓ **Logical Reasoning**
- ✓ **Originality**
- ✓ **Part to Whole Relationships**
- Patterning
- Relationships (Visual)
- Sequencing
- Spatial Relationships
- ✓ **Synthesis**
- ✓ **Transformations**

Notes:

CREATURE FEATURES I

 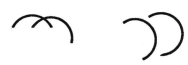 

Zips   Zaps   Zups

Notice the differences in these figures.

1.

Circle the Zips.

2.

Circle the Zaps.

3.

Circle the Zups.

Now draw a new creature for each group.

1. Zip	2. Zap.	3. Zup

© 1990 by Incentive Publications, Inc., Nashville, TN.

* Answer Key

CREATURE FEATURES II

F
k
H
L
Wims

7
N ₄T
Wams

9
8 ⁵₆
Wums

Notice the differences in these figures.

1.

Y
U   **9**
       6   4F   **R**k   Vz   ⁵₇

Circle the Wims.

2.

N
N   L̩S   **8**
              T   ₩̂   **N**
                            Z   ₈   S⁵

Circle the Wams.

3.

8̊   ₉U   ⩏
            E   ₆̂   X̣X   4
                                 ̇Y   **2**
                                        1

Circle the Wums.

Now draw a new creature for each group.

1. Wim	2. Wam	3. Wum

© 1990 by Incentive Publications, Inc., Nashville, TN.   * Answer Key

CREATURE FEATURES III

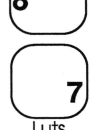

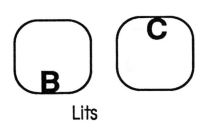

Lits

Lots

Luts

Notice the differences in these figures.

1. W T R 6 σ

Circle the Lits.

2. 4 M Я D O

Circle the Lots.

3. D 1 T 5 S

Circle the Luts.

Now draw a new creature for each group.

1. Lit	2. Lot	3. Lut

© 1990 by Incentive Publications, Inc., Nashville, TN

* Answer Key

CREATURE FEATURES IV

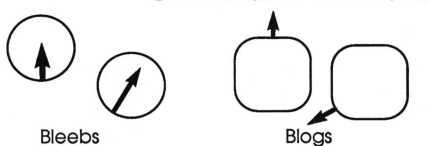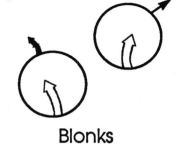

Bleebs   Blogs   Blonks

Notice the differences in these figures.

1.

Circle the Bleebs.

2.

Circle the Blogs.

3.

Circle the Blonks.

Now draw a new creature for each group.

1. Bleeb	2. Blog	3. Blonk

© 1990 by Incentive Publications, Inc., Nashville, TN.

* Answer Key

ENRICHMENT: VERBAL CATEGORIZING

The Problem: Grouping related words and ideas.

The Activity: Read each set of words to the class. Discuss what the words have in common and have the students decide which word in each group doesn't belong. (The underlined word in each group is the word that doesn't belong.)

1. <u>dollar</u>	nickel	dime	quarter
2. pear	apple	banana	<u>carrot</u>
3. meat	potatoes	apple	<u>milk</u>
4. liver	chicken	<u>spaghetti</u>	hamburger
5. <u>horse</u>	puppy	kitten	calf
6. lion	tiger	<u>wolf</u>	bobcat
7. hooves	<u>hands</u>	mane	tail
8. <u>apricot</u>	lettuce	celery	carrot
9. <u>raisins</u>	almonds	walnuts	pecans
10. grass	tree	weed	<u>dirt</u>
11. oven	stove	<u>sink</u>	microwave
12. spoon	<u>table</u>	fork	knife
13. hatchet	saw	knife	<u>tent</u>
14. book	<u>tape</u>	magazine	newspaper
15. <u>sofa</u>	pillow	blanket	sheet
16. mother	father	sister	<u>cousin</u>
17. teacher	<u>mother</u>	principal	student
18. math	reading	spelling	<u>eating</u>
19. pop	milk	<u>cookie</u>	lemonade
20. football	softball	<u>gymnastics</u>	basketball

FIND THE LIKENESS

The Problem: Determining which figure is most closely related to a similar, yet different, figure and creating two original, related figures (figural analogies).

The Activity: Reproduce and distribute pages 110-117. Instruct the students to do the following:

1. Circle the figure that is most like the one in the first box of each row. (Answers may vary. Just ask for justification.)
2. Draw two related figures in the last two boxes of each row. (These figures will vary considerably depending on the "likeness" used.)

Enrichment: Be sure to discuss the differences in the figures as well as the likenesses.

PROCESS/SKILLS CHART

Complex Process
- Critical Thinking
- ✓ **Creative Thinking**

Thought Scheme
- Convergent Thinking
- ✓ **Divergent Thinking**

Content Skills
- Reading Skills Required
- Writing Skills Required
- Counting Skills Required

Basic Skills
- ✓ **Analysis**
- Categorizing
- Classifying
- ✓ **Comparison**

- ✓ **Conditional Logic**
- Deductive Reasoning
- Grouping
- ✓ **Hypothesizing**
- Identification
- ✓ **Imagination**
- Inductive Reasoning
- ✓ **Inference**
- Intuition
- Labeling
- ✓ **Logical Reasoning**
- ✓ **Originality**
- ✓ **Part to Whole Relationships**
- Patterning
- ✓ **Relationships (Visual)**
- ✓ **Sequencing**
- ✓ **Spatial Relationships**
- ✓ **Synthesis**
- ✓ **Transformations**

Notes:

FIND THE LIKENESS I

Circle the figure that is most like the one in the first box of each row.
Then draw two related figures in the last two boxes of each row.
The first one has been done for you.

1. is more like

2. is more like

3. is more like

4. is more like

5. is more like

© 1990 by Incentive Publications, Inc., Nashville, TN.

Note: Answers will vary.

Name _____

FIND THE LIKENESS II

Circle the figure that is most like the one in the first box of each row.
Then draw two related figures in the last two boxes of each row.

1. is more like

2. is more like

3. is more like

4. is more like

5. is more like

© 1990 by Incentive Publications, Inc., Nashville, TN.

Note: Answers will vary.

FIND THE LIKENESS III

Circle the figure that is most like the one in the first box of each row. Then draw two related figures in the last two boxes of each row.

1. is more like

2. is more like

3. is more like

4. is more like

5. is more like

© 1990 by Incentive Publications, Inc., Nashville, TN.

Note: Answers will vary.

FIND THE LIKENESS IV

Circle the figure that is most like the one in the first box of each row.
Then draw two related figures in the last two boxes of each row.

1. is more like

2. is more like

3. is more like

4. is more like

5. is more like

© 1990 by Incentive Publications, Inc., Nashville, TN.

Note: Answers will vary.

Name _____

FIND THE LIKENESS V

Circle the figure that is most like the one in the first box of each row.
Then draw two related figures in the last two boxes of each row.

M	is more like	**E**	**O**		
1.					
K	is more like	**∀**	**◄**		
2.					
PP	is more like	**RR**	**FG**		
3.					
Ww	is more like	**K**k	**H**h		
4.					
S6	is more like	**T9**	**u4**		
5.					

© 1990 by Incentive Publications, Inc., Nashville, TN.

Note: Answers will vary.

Name ______________________

FIND THE LIKENESS VI

Circle the figure that is most like the one in the first box of each row. Then draw two related figures in the last two boxes of each row.

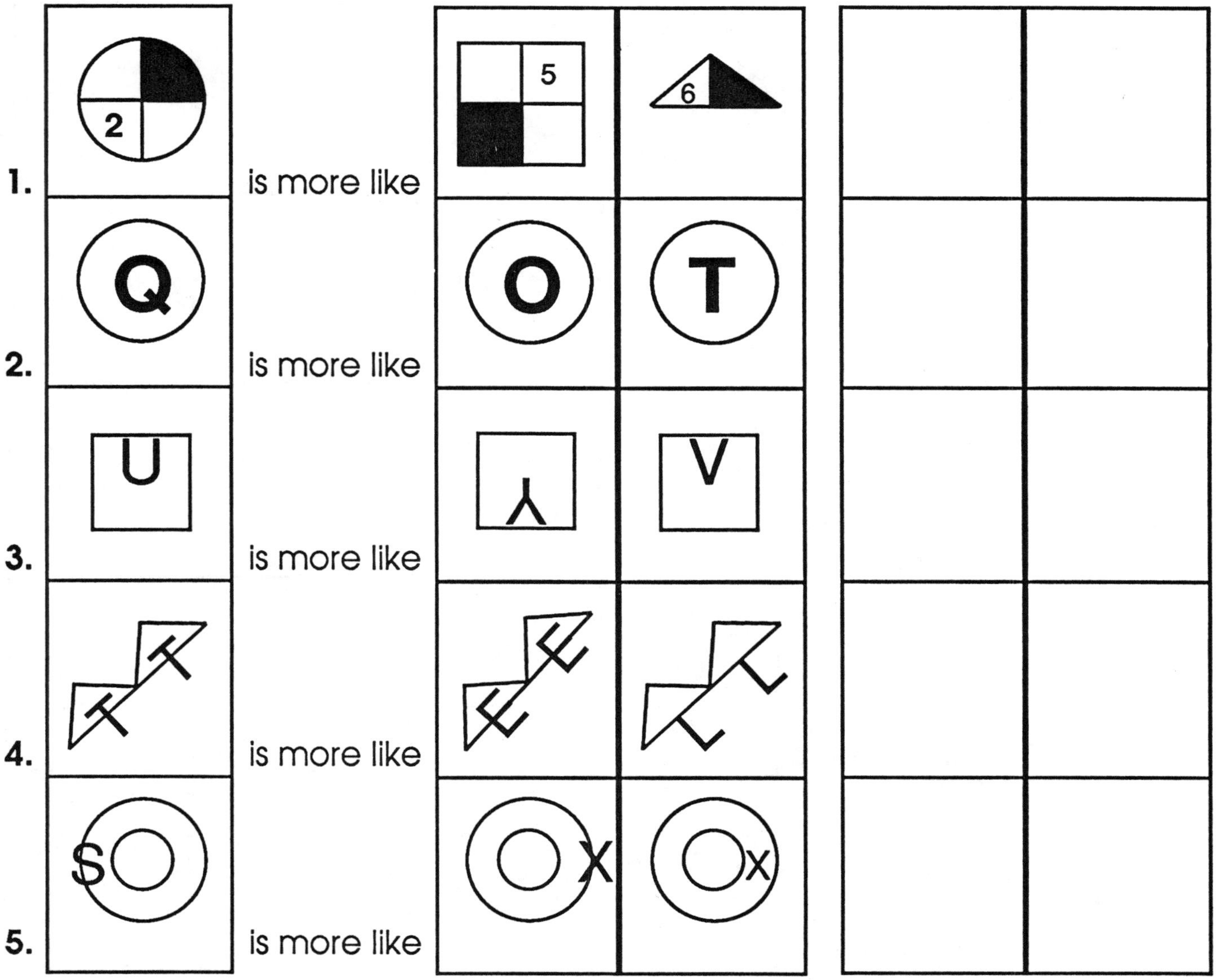
1.
2
is more like
5
6
2.
Q
is more like
O
T
3.
U
is more like
V
4.
is more like
5.
S
is more like
X
X

© 1990 by Incentive Publications, Inc., Nashville, TN.

Note: Answers will vary.

FIND THE LIKENESS VII

Circle the figure that is most like the one in the first box of each row.
Then draw two related figures in the last two boxes of each row.

1. is more like

2. is more like

3. is more like

4. is more like

5. is more like

© 1990 by Incentive Publications, Inc., Nashville, TN.

Note: Answers will vary.

FIND THE LIKENESS VIII

Name _____

Circle the figure that is most like the one in the first box of each row.
Then draw two related figures in the last two boxes of each row.

1. 2345 is more like		7890	2 r s 5		
2. is more like					
3. is more like					
4. h y is more like		f ♩	b d		
5. is more like					

© 1990 by Incentive Publications, Inc., Nashville, TN.

Note: Answers will vary.

YOU MAKE THE DIFFERENCE

The Problem: Making identical figures unique.

The Activity: Reproduce and distribute pages 119-122. Instruct the students to use an original method to make the four identical figures in each row different from one another. Remind the students not to forget color.

Enrichment: This is a good time to point out unique characteristics of people, animals, plants, situations, objects, etc.

PROCESS/SKILLS CHART

Complex Process
   Critical Thinking
   ✓ **Creative Thinking**

Thought Scheme
   Convergent Thinking
   ✓ **Divergent Thinking**

Content Skills
   Reading Skills Required
   Writing Skills Required
   Counting Skills Required

Basic Skills
   ✓ **Analysis**
   Categorizing
   Classifying
   ✓ **Comparison**

✓ **Conditional Logic**
   Deductive Reasoning
   Grouping
   Hypothesizing
   Identification
✓ **Imagination**
   Inductive Reasoning
   Inference
   Intuition
   Labeling
   Logical Reasoning
✓ **Originality**
✓ **Part to Whole Relationships**
✓ **Patterning**
✓ **Relationships (Visual)**
   Sequencing
✓ **Spatial Relationships**
✓ **Synthesis**
✓ **Transformations**

Notes:

YOU MAKE THE DIFFERENCE I

Use an original method to make the four identical figures in each row different from one another.

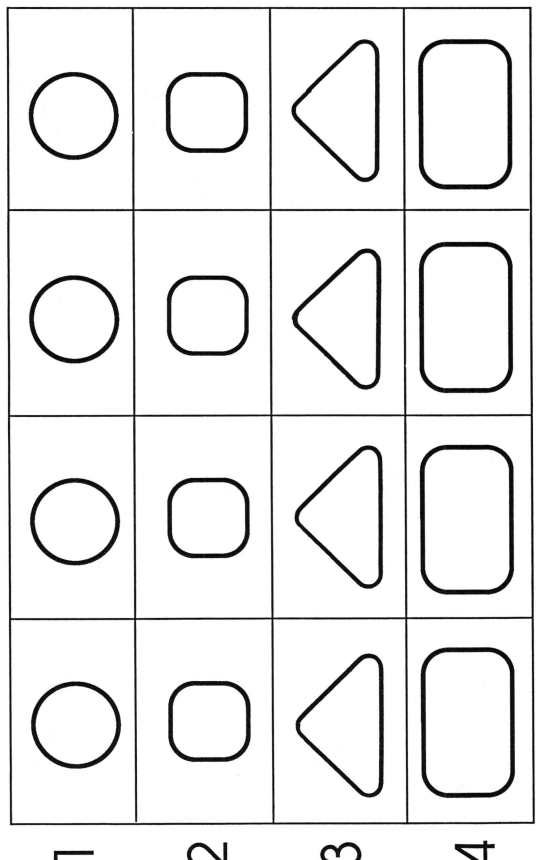

1

2

3

4

© 1990 by Incentive Publications, Inc., Nashville, TN.

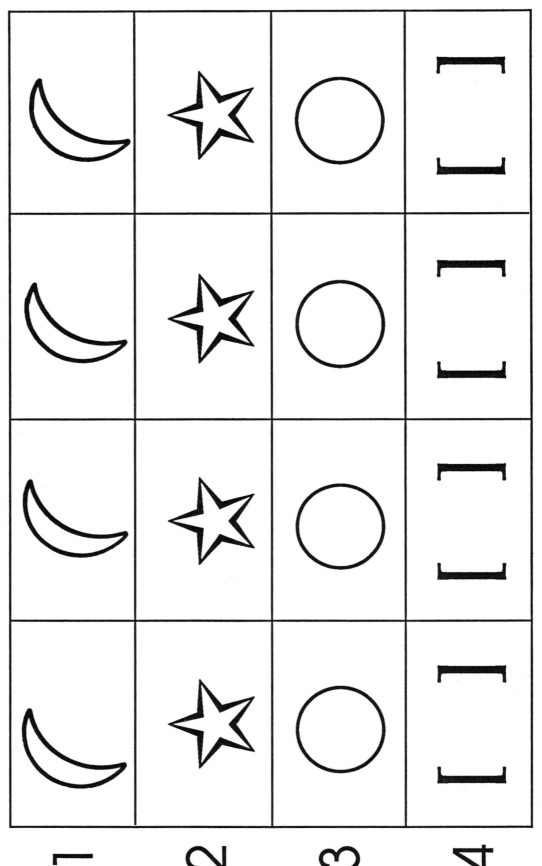

YOU MAKE THE DIFFERENCE II

Use an original method to make the four identical figures in each row different from one another.

© 1990 by Incentive Publications, Inc., Nashville, TN.

YOU MAKE THE DIFFERENCE III

Use an original method to make the four identical figures in each row different from one another.

1			
2			
3			
4			

© 1990 by Incentive Publications, Inc., Nashville, TN.

YOU MAKE THE DIFFERENCE IV

Make each figure in the first and second rows into a different letter.
Make each figure in the third and fourth rows into a different letter.

1	—	—	—	—
2	◯	◯	◯	◯
3	—	—	—	—
4	◯	◯	◯	◯

© 1990 by Incentive Publications, Inc., Nashville, TN.

ENRICHMENT: VERBAL ANALOGIES

The Problem: Completing a verbal analogy.

The Activity: Have the students complete the following statements (answers may vary). You may choose to write the statements on the board or let students respond orally.

1. Bird is to a chirp as dog is to _____ .
2. Wet is to dry as black is to _____ .
3. Apple is to fruit as carrot is to _____ .
4. Always is to never as more is to _____ .
5. Teacher is to school as doctor is to _____ .
6. Terrible is to awful as good is to _____ .
7. Warm is to hot as cool is to _____ .
8. Grape is to raisin as plum is to _____ .
9. Hill is to mountain as stream is to _____ .
10. Teeth is to bite as shovel is to _____ .
11. Penny is to dime as dime is to _____ .
12. Colt is to horse as kitten is to _____ .
13. Dog is to puppy as cow is to _____ .
14. Table is to tables as chair is to _____ .
15. Eskimo is to igloo as Indian is to _____ .
16. Bad is to good as worst is to _____ .
17. Two is to four as three is to _____ .
18. Go is to stop as last is to _____ .
19. Prince is to Princess as King is to _____ .
20. Two is to twin as three is to _____ .
21. Sad is to happy as day is to _____ .
22. Like is to love as dislike is to _____ .
23. Father is to son as mother is to _____ .
24. Guest is to hotel as patient is to _____ .
25. Old is to young as short is to _____ .
26. Scale is to fish as feather is to _____ .
27. Down is to up as low is to _____ .
28. Foot is to toe as hand is to _____ .
29. Wrist is to arm as ankle is to _____ .
30. Bowl is to bowls as dog is to _____ .

THE CHANGING FIGURE: IF/THEN

The Problem: Noting the change in a figure and using logical reasoning to relate the same change to a new situation.

The Activity: Reproduce and distribute pages 125-133. Instruct the students to determine how the first figure in each row has been changed and to draw the second figure with the same type of change.

PROCESS/SKILLS CHART

Complex Process
- ✓ Critical Thinking
- ✓ Creative Thinking

Thought Scheme
- Convergent Thinking
- ✓ Divergent Thinking

Content Skills
- Reading Skills Required
- Writing Skills Required
- Counting Skills Required

Basic Skills
- ✓ Analysis
- Categorizing
- Classifying
- ✓ Comparison

- ✓ Conditional Logic
- ✓ Deductive Reasoning
- Grouping
- ✓ Hypothesizing
- Identification
- ✓ Imagination
- Inductive Reasoning
- ✓ Inference
- Intuition
- Labeling
- ✓ Logical Reasoning
- ✓ Originality
- ✓ Part to Whole Relationships
- Patterning
- ✓ Relationships (Visual)
- Sequencing
- ✓ Spatial Relationships
- ✓ Synthesis
- ✓ Transformations

Notes:

THE CHANGING FIGURE: IF/THEN I

Determine how the first figure has been changed and then draw the second figure with the same type of change.

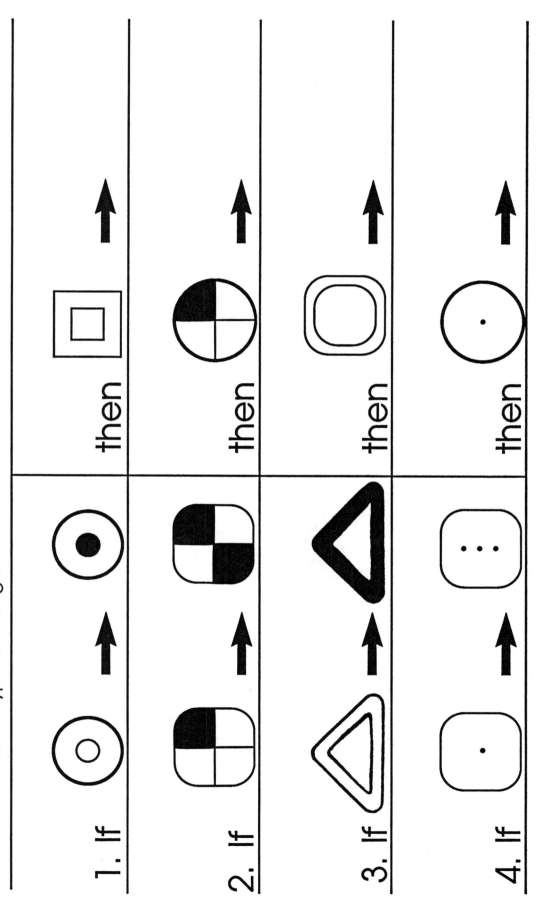

1. If

then

2. If

then

3. If

then

4. If

then

© 1990 by Incentive Publications, Inc., Nashville, TN.

*Answer Key

125

THE CHANGING FIGURE: IF/THEN II

Determine how the first figure has been changed and then draw the second figure with the same type of change.

1. If ○○ → ○—○ then △△△ ↑

2. If ○○ → ⊗ then ☐☐ ↑

3. If ⋈ → ◁▷ then ⊗ ↑

4. If ☐ → ☐☐ then △◁ ↑

© 1990 by Incentive Publications, Inc., Nashville, TN.

*Answer Key

THE CHANGING FIGURE: IF/THEN III

Determine how the first figure has been changed and then draw the second figure with the same type of change.

1. If ◯ → ◯ **then** ☐ ↑

2. If ☐☐ → ☐☐ **then** ◯ ◦ ↑

3. If ⊖ → ⊖ **then** ⬭ ↑

4. If ◉ → ◯• **then** ☐■ ↑

© 1990 by Incentive Publications, Inc., Nashville, TN.

*Answer Key

127

THE CHANGING FIGURE: IF/THEN IV

Determine how the first figure has been changed and then draw the second figure with the same type of change.

1. If ⬦ → ↑ → ◇ ... then → ↑

2. If ▫▫▫ → ↑ → ▢▢▢ ... then ○○○ → ↑

3. If ◀ → ↑ → ◀ ... then ◖ → ↑

4. If △▢ → ↑ → ▢▷ ... then ○▯ → ↑

© 1990 by Incentive Publications, Inc., Nashville, TN.

*Answer Key

THE CHANGING FIGURE: IF/THEN V

Determine how the first figure has been changed and then draw the second figure with the same type of change.

1. If M ⬆ m then R ⬆

2. If E
      E ⬆ EE then N
               N ⬆

3. If T ⬆ ⊥ then A ⬆

4. If n ⬆ N then b ⬆

© 1990 by Incentive Publications, Inc., Nashville, TN.

*Answer Key

THE CHANGING FIGURE: IF/THEN VI

Determine how the first figure has been changed and then draw the second figure with the same type of change.

1. If **EEE** → **EEE** then **HHH** →

2. If **MN** → **NM** then **XY** →

3. If **AB** → **BA** then **12** →

4. If **MM** → **WW** then **UU** →

© 1990 by Incentive Publications, Inc., Nashville, TN.

*Answer Key

THE CHANGING FIGURE: IF/THEN VII

Determine how the first figure has been changed and then draw the second figure with the same type of change.

1. If **234** ↑   **432**   then **567** ↑

2. If **77** ↑   **77**   then **22** ↑

3. If **11**   **11** ↑   **1111**   then **55** **55** ↑

4. If **383** ↑   **838**   then **494** ↑

© 1990 by Incentive Publications, Inc., Nashville, TN.

*Answer Key

THE CHANGING FIGURE: IF/THEN VIII

Determine how the first figure has been changed and then draw the second figure with the same type of change.

1. If   69   →   69   then   65   →

2. If   →   then   →

3. If   →   then   →

4. If   →   then   →

© 1999 by Incentive Publications, Inc., Nashville, TN

*Answer Key

THE CHANGING FIGURE: IF/THEN IX

Determine how the first figure has been changed and then draw the second figure with the same type of change.

1. If 7 ⟶ 7 **then** 3 ⟶

2. If 7 6 R 6 ⟶ 7 6 R **then** 3 2 N ⟶

3. If 9 8 ⟶ 8 9 **then** 5 ④ ⟶

4. If PP 5 ⟶ P5 P ⟶ **then** JJ 2 ⟶

© 1990 by Incentive Publications, Inc., Nashville, TN.

*Answer Key

WEIGHT CONTROL

The Problem: Using logical reasoning and visual clues to deduce the weight relationship of different figures.

The Activity: Reproduce and distribute pages 135-139. Instruct the students to do the following:

1. Circle the answers to questions 1 and 2.
2. Use the answers for questions 1 and 2 to answer question 3. Draw the figures in the correct weight relationship on seesaw 3.

Enrichment: Do the same type of activity using the students' actual weights.

PROCESS/SKILLS CHART

Complex Process
- ✓ **Critical Thinking**
-   Creative Thinking

Thought Scheme
- ✓ **Convergent Thinking**
-   Divergent Thinking

Content Skills
- ✓ **Reading Skills Required**
-   Writing Skills Required
-   Counting Skills Required

Basic Skills
- ✓ **Analysis**
-   Categorizing
-   Classifying
- ✓ **Comparison**

   Conditional Logic
- ✓ **Deductive Reasoning**
-   Grouping
- ✓ **Hypothesizing**
-   Identification
-   Imagination
-   Inductive Reasoning
- ✓ **Inference**
-   Intuition
-   Labeling
- ✓ **Logical Reasoning**
-   Originality
-   Part to Whole Relationships
-   Patterning
-   Relationships (Visual)
-   Sequencing
-   Spatial Relationships
- ✓ **Synthesis**
- ✓ **Transformations**

Notes:

WEIGHT CONTROL I

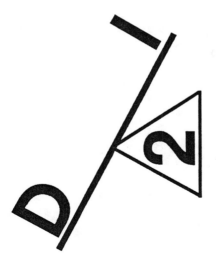

1. Which letter weighs more? **A   I** (Circle one.)
   How do you know?

2. Which letter weighs more? **D   I** (Circle one.)
   How do you know?

3. Which letter weighs the most?
   A   D   I (Circle one.)
   Draw figures A and D in the correct weight
   relationship on the seesaw.

© 1990 by Incentive Publications, Inc., Nashville, TN.

*Answer Key

WEIGHT CONTROL II

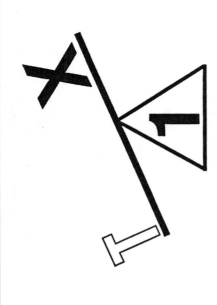

1. Which letter weighs less? T **X**   (Circle one.)
    How do you know?

2. Which letter weighs less? **X** H   (Circle one.)
    How do you know?

3. Which letter weighs least? T **X** H   (Circle one.)
    Draw figures X and H in the correct weight
    relationship on the seesaw.

© 1990 by Incentive Publications, Inc., Nashville, TN.

*Answer Key

WEIGHT CONTROL III

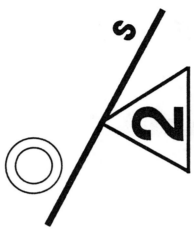

1. Which letter weighs more? 𝔽 **s** (Circle one.)
   How do you know?

2. Which letter weighs more? ◎ **s** (Circle one.)
   How do you know?

3. Which letter weighs most? 𝔽 **s** ◎ (Circle one.)
   Draw figures 𝔽 and ◎ in the correct weight
   relationship on the seesaw.

© 1990 by Incentive Publications, Inc., Nashville, TN.

*Answer Key

WEIGHT CONTROL IV

1. Which letter weighs less? **L   S**   (Circle one.)
   How do you know?

2. Which letter weighs less? **J   S**   (Circle one.)
   How do you know?

3. Which letter weighs least? **L   S   J**   (Circle one.)
   Draw figures **L** and **J** in the correct weight
   relationship on the seesaw.

© 1990 by Incentive Publications, Inc., Nashville, TN.

*Answer Key

WEIGHT CONTROL V

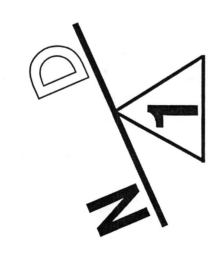

1. Which letter weighs more? **N** Ⓓ (Circle one.)
    How do you know?

2. Which letter weighs more? **N** W (Circle one.)
    How do you know?

3. Which letter weighs the most? **N** Ⓓ W (Circle one.)
    Draw figures W and Ⓓ in the correct weight
    relationship on the seesaw.

© 1990 by Incentive Publications, Inc., Nashville, TN.

*Answer Key

GADGET INSPECTION

The Problem: Making the gadgets work by turning wheels in the right direction; using visual clues and logical reasoning to determine direction.

The Activity: Reproduce and distribute pages 141-144. Instruct the students to do the following:

1. Note the direction of wheel number 1.
2. Use that information to determine the direction of the other wheels.
3. Draw two arrows on each wheel showing the direction it is turning.

PROCESS/SKILLS CHART

Complex Process
  Critical Thinking
  ✓ **Creative Thinking**

Thought Scheme
  Convergent Thinking
  ✓ **Divergent Thinking**

Content Skills
  Reading Skills Required
  Writing Skills Required
  Counting Skills Required

Basic Skills
  ✓ **Analysis**
  Categorizing
  Classifying
  ✓ **Comparison**

✓ **Conditional Logic**
✓ **Deductive Reasoning**
  Grouping
✓ **Hypothesizing**
  Identification
✓ **Imagination**
  Inductive Reasoning
✓ **Inference**
  Intuition
  Labeling
✓ **Logical Reasoning**
  Originality
✓ **Part to Whole Relationships**
  Patterning
  Relationships (Visual)
✓ **Sequencing**
✓ **Spatial Relationships**
✓ **Synthesis**
✓ **Transformations**

Notes:

GADGET INSPECTION I

Note the direction of wheel number 1.
Use that information to determine the direction of the other wheels.
Draw two arrows on each wheel to show the direction it is turning.

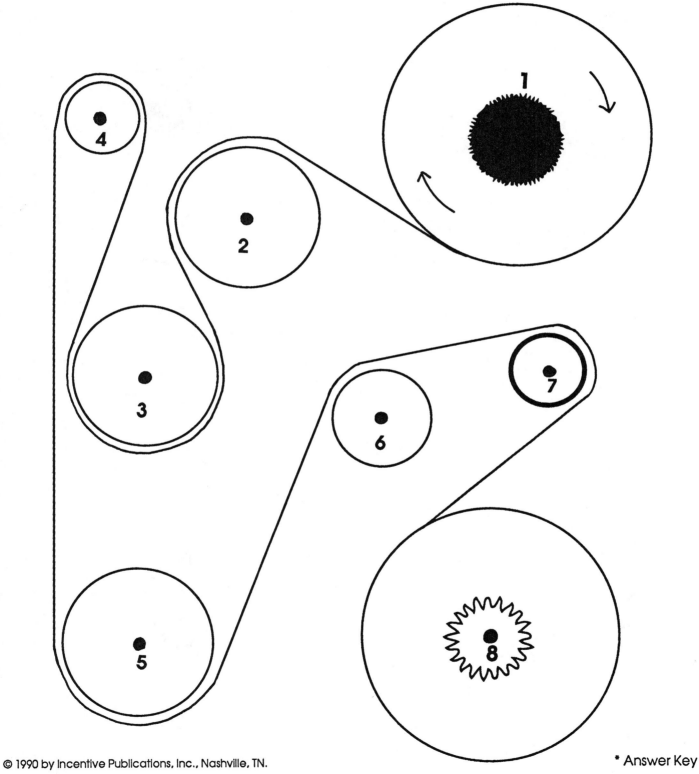

© 1990 by Incentive Publications, Inc., Nashville, TN.

* Answer Key

GADGET INSPECTION II

Note the direction of wheel number 1.
Use that information to determine the
   direction of the other wheels.
Draw two arrows on each wheel to
   show the direction it is turning.

1

5

3

7

2

6

4

8

10

9

© 1990 by Incentive Publications, Inc., Nashville, TN.

* Answer Key

GADGET INSPECTION III

Note the direction of wheel number 1.
Use that information to determine the
  direction of the other wheels.
Draw two arrows on each wheel to
  show the direction it is turning.

* Answer Key
© 1990 by Incentive Publications, Inc., Nashville, TN.

Challenge

GADGET INSPECTION IV

Note the direction of wheel number 1.
Use that information to determine the
   direction of the other wheels.
Draw two arrows on each wheel to
   show the direction it is turning.

1

2

3

4

5

7

6

8

9

© 1990 by Incentive Publications, Inc., Nashville, TN.

144

* Answer Key

GADGET REPAIR

The Problem: Using visual clues and logical reasoning to determine the way that a ribbon would pass through a set of turning wheels.

The Activity: Reproduce and distribute pages 146-150. Instruct the students to do the following:

1. Note the direction that each wheel is turning.
2. Draw the ribbon through the gadget using every wheel once. Remember, no lines can be crossed!

PROCESS/SKILLS CHART

Complex Process
Critical Thinking
✓ **Creative Thinking**

Thought Scheme
Convergent Thinking
✓ **Divergent Thinking**

Content Skills
Reading Skills Required
Writing Skills Required
Counting Skills Required

Basic Skills
✓ **Analysis**
Categorizing
Classifying
✓ **Comparison**

✓ **Conditional Logic**
✓ **Deductive Reasoning**
Grouping
✓ **Hypothesizing**
Identification
✓ **Imagination**
Inductive Reasoning
✓ **Inference**
Intuition
Labeling
✓ **Logical Reasoning**
Originality
✓ **Part to Whole Relationships**
Patterning
Relationships (Visual)
✓ **Sequencing**
✓ **Spatial Relationships**
✓ **Synthesis**
✓ **Transformations**

Notes:

GADGET REPAIR I

Notice the direction each wheel is turning.
Draw a ribbon as it would pass through the gadget.
Use each wheel only once and do not cross lines!

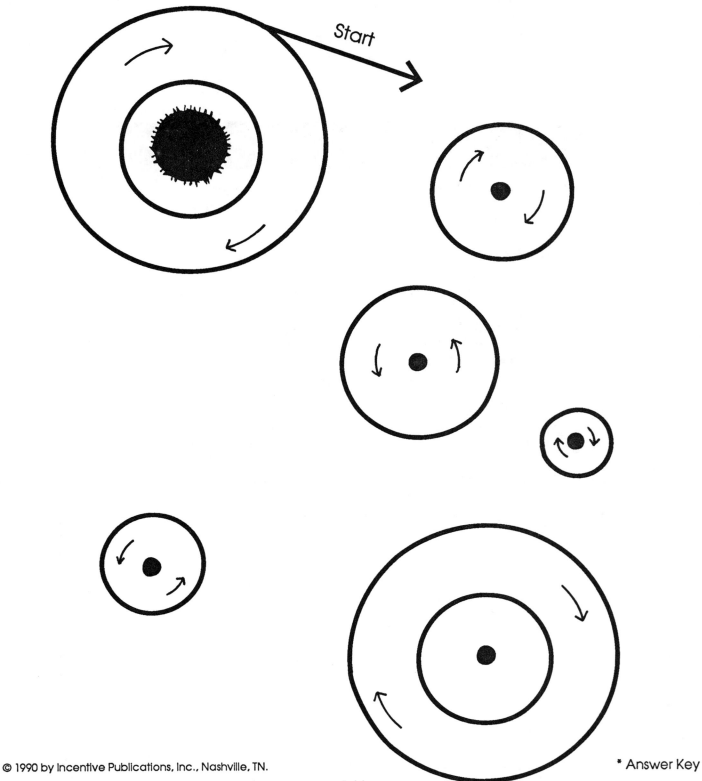

© 1990 by Incentive Publications, Inc., Nashville, TN.

* Answer Key

Name _____

GADGET REPAIR II

Notice the direction each wheel is turning.
Draw a ribbon as it would pass through the gadget.
Use each wheel only once and do not cross lines!

* Answer Key
© 1990 by Incentive Publications, Inc., Nashville, TN.

Name _____

GADGET REPAIR III

Notice the direction each wheel is turning.
Draw a ribbon as it would pass through the gadget.
Use each wheel only once and do not cross lines!

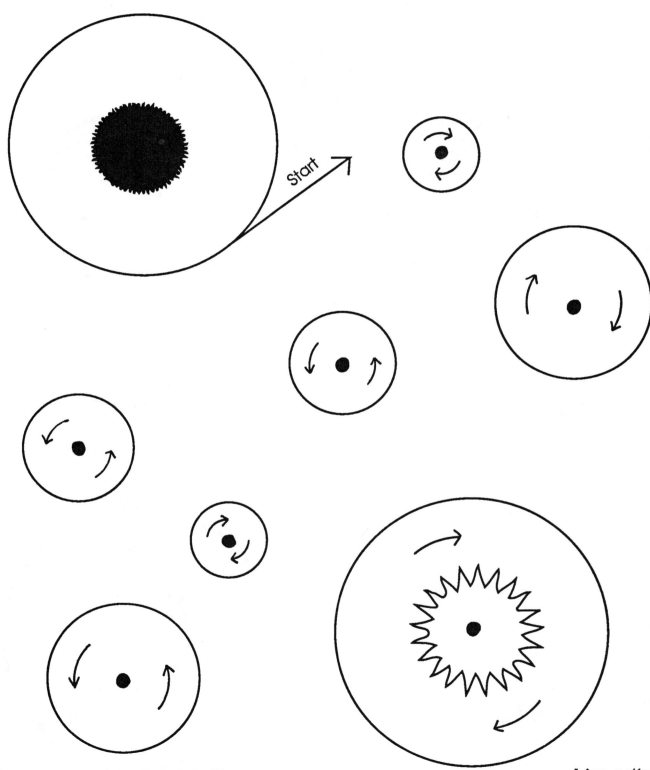

© 1990 by Incentive Publications, Inc., Nashville, TN.

* Answer Key

GADGET REPAIR IV

Notice the direction each wheel is turning.
Draw a ribbon as it would pass through the gadget.
Use each wheel only once and do not cross lines!

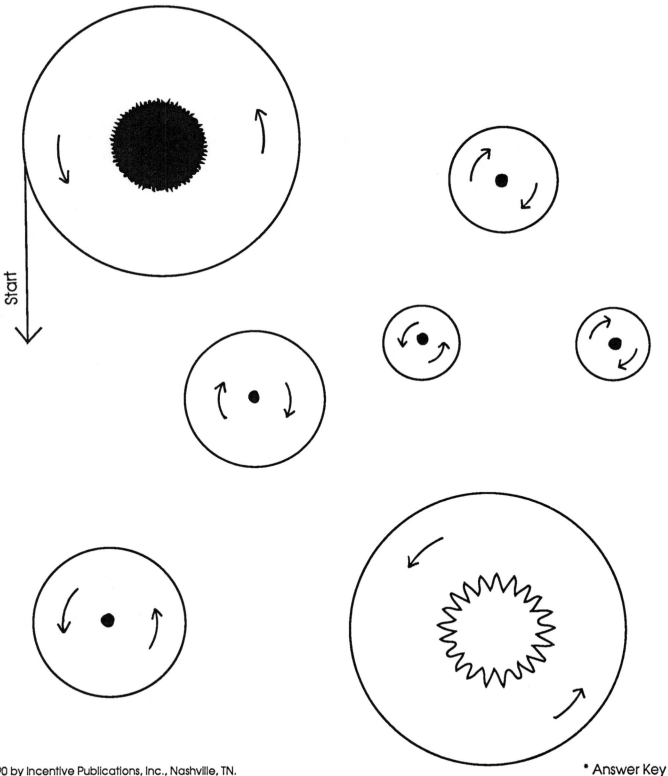

© 1990 by Incentive Publications, Inc., Nashville, TN.

* Answer Key

Challenge

GADGET REPAIR V

Notice the direction each wheel is turning.
Draw a ribbon as it would pass through the gadget.
Use each wheel only once and do not cross lines!

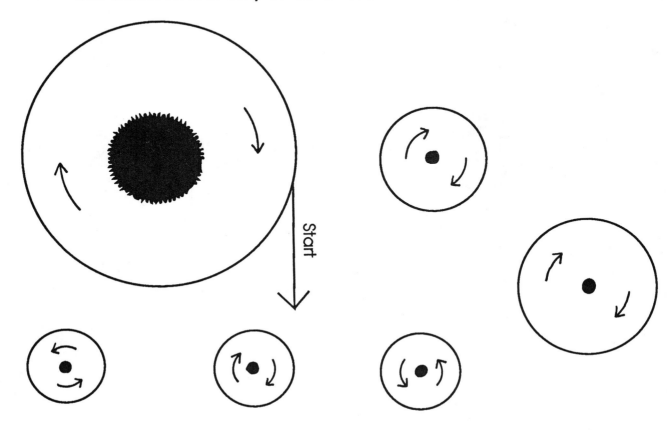

Start

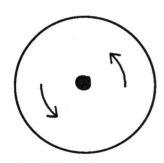

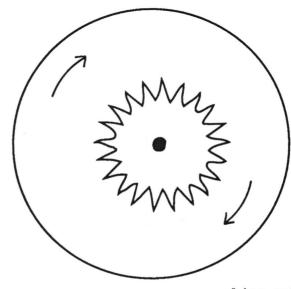

© 1990 by Incentive Publications, Inc., Nashville, TN.

* Answer Key

CLUES FROM THE PLANET ROO/ CLUES FROM THE PLANET NU

The Problem: Using deductive reasoning, visual and verbal clues to label a series of figures.

The Activity: Reproduce and distribute pages 152-160. Instruct the students to read the clues and write the correct name under each figure.

PROCESS/SKILLS CHART

Complex Process
- ✓ Critical Thinking
- Creative Thinking

Thought Scheme
- ✓ Convergent Thinking
- Divergent Thinking

Content Skills
- ✓ Reading Skills Required
- Writing Skills Required
- Counting Skills Required

Basic Skills
- ✓ Analysis
- Categorizing
- Classifying
- ✓ Comparison

- ✓ Conditional Logic
- ✓ Deductive Reasoning
- Grouping
- ✓ Hypothesizing
- ✓ Identification
- Imagination
- Inductive Reasoning
- ✓ Inference
- Intuition
- ✓ Labeling
- ✓ Logical Reasoning
- Originality
- ✓ Part to Whole Relationships
- Patterning
- Relationships (Visual)
- ✓ Sequencing
- ✓ Spatial Relationships
- ✓ Synthesis
- Transformations

Notes:

Name _____

CLUES FROM THE PLANET ROO I

Read the clues and write the correct name under each Roo-bot.

A.

1. Boo is between Doo and Too.
2. Doo is not first.

1. _____   2. _____   3. _____

B.

1. No Roo-bot is following Goo.
2. Koo is not next to Goo.
3. One Roo-bot is named Loo.

1. _____   2. _____   3. _____

© 1990 by Incentive Publications, Inc., Nashville, TN.

* Answer Key

CLUES FROM THE PLANET ROO II

Read the clues and write the correct name under each Roo-bot.

A.

1. BD2 is closest to C3Pd.
2. V8 is following B12.
3. B12 is farthest from C3Pd.

1._____ 2. _____ 3. _____ 4. __C 3 Pd__

B.

1. TP3 is last.
2. Wv2 is in front of Kkt.

1. _____ 2. _____ 3. _____

© 1990 by Incentive Publications, Inc., Nashville, TN.

* Answer Key

Name _____

CLUES FROM THE PLANET ROO III

Read the clues and write the correct name under each Roo-bot.

1. All of the round Roo-bots have number names.
2. The biggest Roo-bot has the highest number name.
3. The two smallest Roo-bots have the shortest names.
4. The biggest square Roo-bot does not have the longest letter name.

Name List:

7	z
88	Yy
999	Xxx

 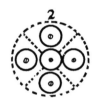 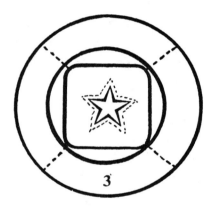

1. _____ 2. _____ 3. _____

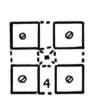 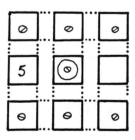

4. _____ 5. _____ 6. _____

© 1990 by Incentive Publications, Inc., Nashville, TN.

* Answer Key

CLUES FROM THE PLANET ROO IV

Read the clues and write the correct name under each Roo-bot.

1. FXi is marked with an X.
2. FXi is between PIP and SIP.
3. SIP is following BLIP.
4. One of the Roo-bots is named KIP.

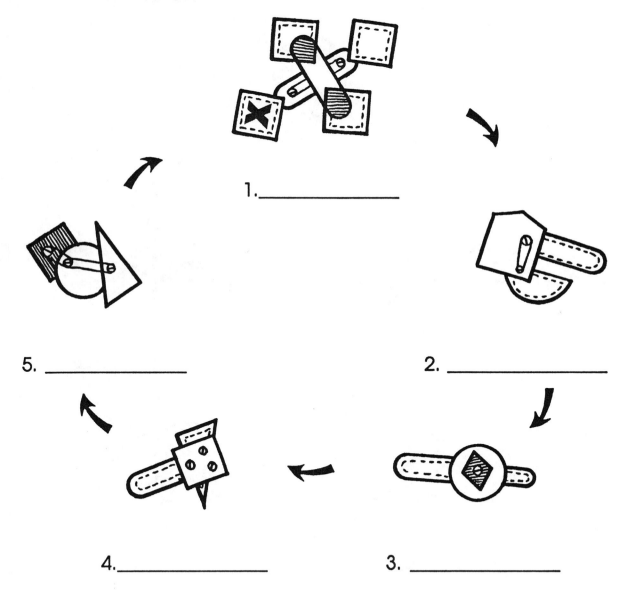

1._____

2. _____

3. _____

4._____

5. _____

© 1990 by Incentive Publications, Inc., Nashville, TN.

* Answer Key

CLUES FROM THE PLANET ROO V

Read the clues and write the correct name under each Roo-bot.

1. One of the Roo-bots is named Y9.
2. Q92 is marked with part of its name.
3. Voo and Doo are not next to Q92.
4. ZP7 is following Voo.

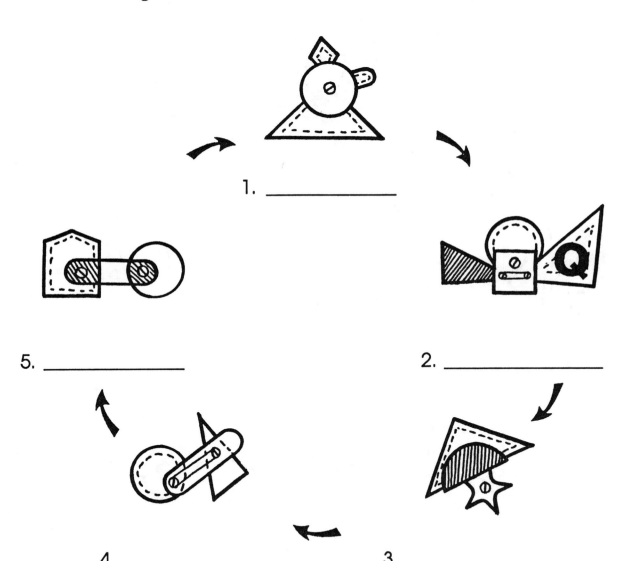

1. _____

2. _____

3. _____

4. _____

5. _____

© 1990 by Incentive Publications, Inc., Nashville, TN.

* Answer Key

CLUES FROM THE PLANET ROO VI

Read the clues and write the correct name under each Roo-bot.

1. One of the Roo-bots is named PU.
2. 4U is the biggest Roo-bot.
3. IM9 is the smallest Roo-bot.
4. UR8 is not next to IM9.
5. We6 is between UR8 and IM9.

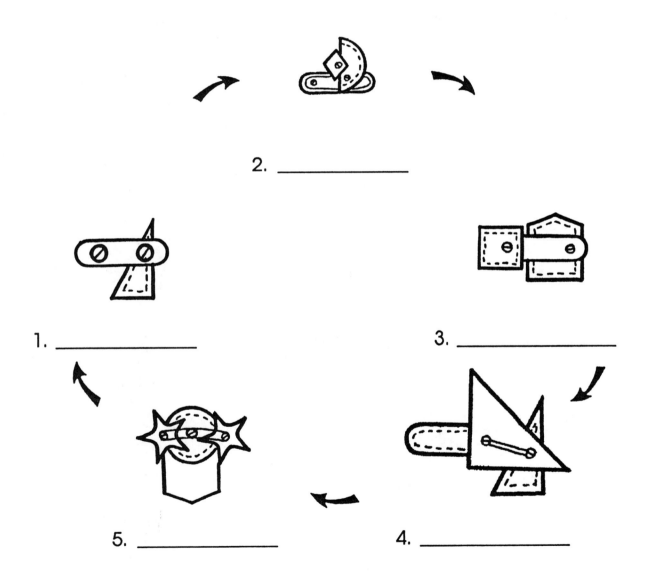

2. _____

1. _____

3. _____

5. _____

4. _____

© 1990 by Incentive Publications, Inc., Nashville, TN.

* Answer Key

CLUES FROM THE PLANET ROO VII

Read the clues and write the correct name on each Roo-bot and Blu-bot's seat.

1. The wheel turns in the direction of the arrows.
2. Nu9 is in the lowest seat moving upwards.
3. Captain Koo is in the highest seat.
4. Soo is between Su8 and Eoo.
5. Koo is between two Blu-bots. Bu2 is one of them.
6. Xoo is on this Roo-bot ride, too.

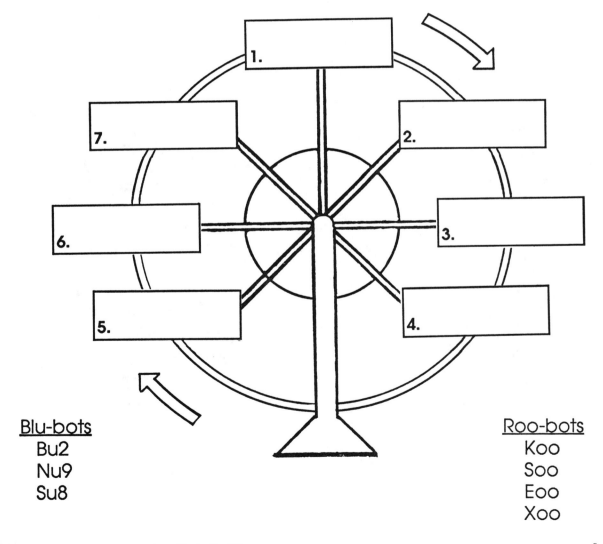

Blu-bots
  Bu2
  Nu9
  Su8

Roo-bots
  Koo
  Soo
  Eoo
  Xoo

© 1990 by Incentive Publications, Inc., Nashville, TN.

* Answer Key

CLUES FROM THE PLANET NU I

Read the clues and write the correct name beside each Nu-bot.

1. Captain 3P is at the top of the page.
2. 8S is farthest from the Captain.
3. 9C is not next to 6F.
4. 6F is always beside the Captain.
5. 7Z is pictured here.

1. _____

2. _____

3. _____

4. _____

5. _____

© 1990 by Incentive Publications, Inc., Nashville, TN.

* Answer Key

CLUES FROM THE PLANET NU II

Read the clues and write the correct name under each Nu-bot.

1. R10, who is next to T7, is on one end.
2. R10 is marked with an X.
3. M9 is marked with an S.
4. M9 is between P8 and T7.
5. L6 is marked with an X.
6. L6 is next to a Nu-bot marked with an S.

1. _____ 2. _____ 3. _____ 4. _____ 5. _____

© 1990 by Incentive Publications, Inc., Nashville, TN.

* Answer Key

SPACES AND PLACES: SPATIAL RELATIONSHIPS

The Problem: Using visual and verbal clues and logical reasoning to determine the position of numbers and/or letters in a combination of geometric shapes.

The Activity: Reproduce and distribute pages 162-165. Instruct the students to study each illustration and to answer the corresponding questions.

PROCESS/SKILLS CHART

Complex Process
- ✓ **Critical Thinking**
- Creative Thinking

Thought Scheme
- Convergent Thinking
- ✓ **Divergent Thinking**

Content Skills
- ✓ **Reading Skills Required**
- Writing Skills Required
- Counting Skills Required

Basic Skills
- ✓ **Analysis**
- ✓ **Categorizing**
- Classifying
- ✓ **Comparison**

- ✓ **Conditional Logic**
- ✓ **Deductive Reasoning**
- ✓ **Grouping**
- ✓ **Hypothesizing**
- ✓ **Identification**
- Imagination
- Inductive Reasoning
- ✓ **Inference**
- Intuition
- Labeling
- ✓ **Logical Reasoning**
- Originality
- ✓ **Part to Whole Relationships**
- Patterning
- ✓ **Relationships (Visual)**
- Sequencing
- ✓ **Spatial Relationships**
- ✓ **Synthesis**
- Transformations

Notes:

Name _____

SPACES AND PLACES:
SPATIAL RELATIONSHIPS I

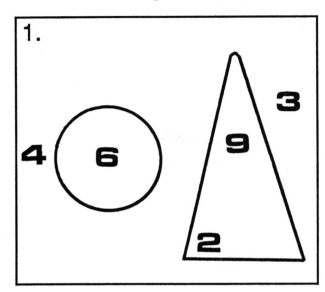

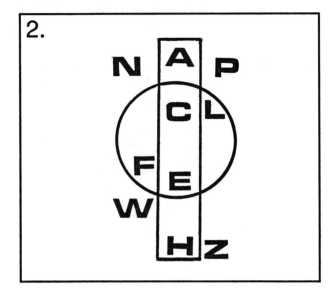

1. a. What numbers are in the ◯ ? _____

    b. What numbers are in the △ ? _____

    c. What numbers are in neither? _____

    d. What numbers are not in the △ ? _____

2. a. What letters are in the ◯ ? _____

    b. What letters are in the ▯ ? _____

    c. What letters are in both? _____

    d. What letters are in neither? _____

    e. What letters are not in the ◯ ? _____

© 1990 by Incentive Publications, Inc., Nashville, TN.

* Answer Key

SPACES AND PLACES:
SPATIAL RELATIONSHIPS II

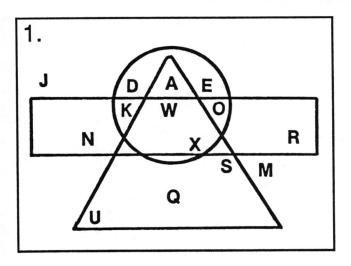

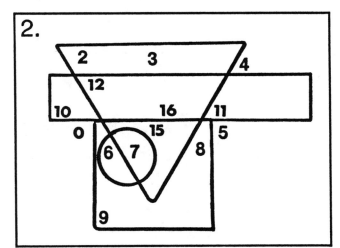

1. a. What letters are in the △ ? _____

   b. What letters are in the ○ ? _____

   c. What letters are in both the ○ and ▢ ? _____

   d. What letters are in both the △ and ○ ? _____

   e. What letters are in all three shapes? _____

2. a. What numbers are in both the ○ and ▽ ? _____

   b. What numbers are in the ▢ , ▽ and ○ ? _____

   c. What numbers are in both the ▢ and ▢ ? _____

   d. What numbers are in no shapes? _____

   e. What numbers are in the ▢ and ○ but are not in the ▽ ? _____

© 1990 by Incentive Publications, Inc., Nashville, TN.

* Answer Key

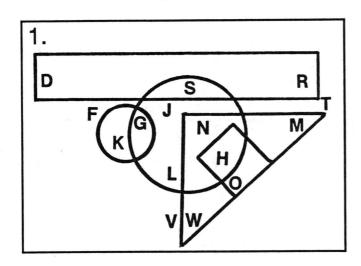

SPACES AND PLACES:
SPATIAL RELATIONSHIPS III

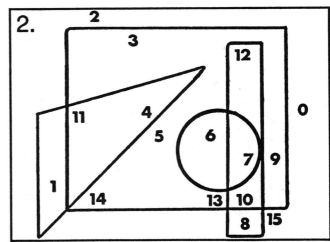

1. a. What letters are in both O's ? _____

    b. What letters are in both ▭ and O ? _____

    c. What letters are in both ▭ and ▷ but not in O ? _____

    d. What letters are in both ▭ and ▷ ? _____

    e. What letters are in the big O, the ▭ and the ▷ ? _____

    f. What letters are in no shape? _____

2. a. What numbers are not in the ▭ ? _____

    b. What numbers are in both the O and ▯ ? _____

    c. What numbers are in both O and ▭ but not in the ▯ ? _____

    d. What numbers are in both the ▷ and O ? _____

    e. What numbers are in no shape? _____

© 1990 by Incentive Publications, Inc., Nashville, TN.

* Answer Key

Name _____

SPACES AND PLACES:
SPATIAL RELATIONSHIPS IV

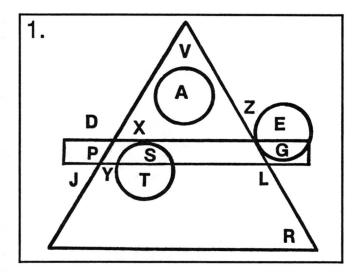

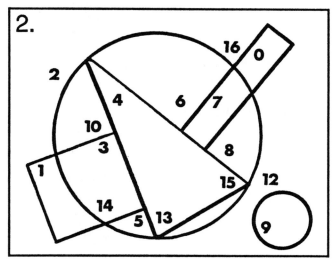

1. a. What letters are in the △ ?

   b. What letters are in both the ▭ and the biggest △ ?

   c. What letters are in both O's and the big △ ?

   d. What letters are in the smallest △ ?

   e. What letters are in the O but not in any △ ?

2. a. What numbers are not in the small O?

   b. What numbers are not in the big O ?

   c. What numbers are in both the △ and the ▢ ?

   d. What numbers are in the ▭ but not in the big O ?

   e. What numbers are not in the ▢ or the ▭ ?

© 1990 by Incentive Publications, Inc., Nashville, TN.

* Answer Key

ENRICHMENT: VERBAL REASONING

The Problem: Composing a chain of reasoning as a group.

The Activity: Directions follow.

A. One player makes a simple statement such as "I like school."

The next player repeats the statement and adds a because clause.

   Example: "I like school because I like to learn new things."

The next player uses the because clause and adds his or her own because clause.

   Example: "I like to learn new things because then I can do things that I couldn't do before."

Continue in this manner until each student has participated.

B. To emphasize sequencing rather than reasoning, begin the added clauses with "after that." Then the students must add a logical connecting sentence.

FIGURES AND FEELINGS

The Problem: Determining the most appropriate symbol (figural analogy) for a word or concept.

The Activity: Reproduce and distribute pages 168-175. Instruct the students to do the following:

    1. Draw a line from each word to the figure that best represents it.
    2. Draw an original figure for each word.

Enrichment: Discuss or create original symbols for other familiar words, feelings, concepts or activities.

PROCESS/SKILLS CHART

Complex Process
- Critical Thinking
- ✓ **Creative Thinking**

Thought Scheme
- Convergent Thinking
- ✓ **Divergent Thinking**

Content Skills
- Reading Skills Required
- Writing Skills Required
- Counting Skills Required

Basic Skills
- ✓ **Analysis**
- Categorizing
- Classifying
- ✓ **Comparison**

Conditional Logic
Deductive Reasoning
Grouping
Hypothesizing
- ✓ **Identification**
- ✓ **Imagination**
- Inductive Reasoning
- ✓ **Inference**
- ✓ **Intuition**
- ✓ **Labeling**
- Logical Reasoning
- ✓ **Originality**
- ✓ **Part to Whole Relationships**
- Patterning
- ✓ **Relationships (Visual)**
- Sequencing
- ✓ **Spatial Relationships**
- ✓ **Synthesis**
- ✓ **Transformations**

Notes:

FIGURES AND FEELINGS I

Draw a line from each figure to the word that best describes it.
Then draw a new figure for each word.

1.		
  crawl walk		crawl
		walk
2.		
  run hop		run
		hop
3.		
  drive fly		drive
		fly

© 1990 by Incentive Publications, Inc., Nashville, TN.

* Answer Key

FIGURES AND FEELINGS II

Draw a line from each figure to the word that best describes it.
Then draw a new figure for each word.

1.

rest   play

rest
play

2.

together   apart

together
apart

3.

older   younger

older
younger

© 1990 by Incentive Publications, Inc., Nashville, TN.

* Answer Key

FIGURES AND FEELINGS III

Draw a line from each figure to the word that best describes it.
Then draw a new figure for each word.

1.	
high low	high
	low
2.	
dull sharp	dull
	sharp
3.	
asleep awake	asleep
	awake

© 1990 by Incentive Publications, Inc., Nashville, TN.

* Answer Key

Name _____

FIGURES AND FEELINGS IV

Draw a line from each figure to the word that best describes it.
Then draw a new figure for each word.

1. ∩ ∪ happy sad	happy sad
2. H ⊢⊣ strong weak	strong weak
3. fast slow	fast slow

© 1990 by Incentive Publications, Inc., Nashville, TN.

* Answer Key

FIGURES AND FEELINGS V

Draw a line from each figure to the word that best describes it.
Then draw a new figure for each word.

1. rocket jet	rocket
	jet
2. turtle rabbit	turtle
	rabbit
3. fish bird	fish
	bird

© 1990 by Incentive Publications, Inc., Nashville, TN.

* Answer Key

Name _____

FIGURES AND FEELINGS VI

Draw a line from each figure to the word that best describes it.
Then draw a new figure for each word.

1.

elephant   mouse

| elephant |
| mouse |

2.

land   water

| land |
| water |

3.

teacher   student

| teacher |
| student |

© 1990 by Incentive Publications, Inc., Nashville, TN.

* Answer Key

Name _____

FIGURES AND FEELINGS VII

Draw a line from each figure to the word that best describes it.
Then draw a new figure for each word.

1.

[IIII]	**DD**
light	dark

light

dark

2.

↑	⊥
living	not living

living

not living

3.

C	ↄ
mother	baby

mother

baby

© 1990 by Incentive Publications, Inc., Nashville, TN.

* Answer Key

FIGURES AND FEELINGS VIII

Draw a line from each figure to the word that best describes it.
Then draw a new figure for each word.

1.

easy   hard

easy

hard

2.

father   son

father

son

3.

plant   animal

plant

animal

© 1990 by Incentive Publications, Inc., Nashville, TN.

* Answer Key

COLORS AND FEELINGS

The Problem: Determining the most appropriate visual representation of a word or concept with the added dimension of color.

The Activity: Reproduce and distribute pages 177-184. Instruct the students to do the following:

1. Color each figure as directed using the color key at the top of the page.
2. Draw a line from each word to the colored figure that best represents it.
3. Draw and color an original figure in the boxes to represent each word.

PROCESS/SKILLS CHART

Complex Process
   Critical Thinking
   ✓ **Creative Thinking**

Thought Scheme
   Convergent Thinking
   ✓ **Divergent Thinking**

Content Skills
   Reading Skills Required
   Writing Skills Required
   Counting Skills Required

Basic Skills
   ✓ **Analysis**
   Categorizing
   Classifying
   ✓ **Comparison**

   Conditional Logic
   Deductive Reasoning
   Grouping
   Hypothesizing
   ✓ **Identification**
   ✓ **Imagination**
   Inductive Reasoning
   ✓ **Inference**
   ✓ **Intuition**
   ✓ **Labeling**
   Logical Reasoning
   ✓ **Originality**
   ✓ **Part to Whole Relationships**
   Patterning
   ✓ **Relationships (Visual)**
   Sequencing
   ✓ **Spatial Relationships**
   ✓ **Synthesis**
   ✓ **Transformations**

Notes:

COLORS AND FEELINGS I

Follow the color key below to color each figure.
Draw a line from each figure to the word that best describes it.
Then make a new figure to represent each word.

O=Orange P=Pink R=Red W=White Blu=Blue Blk=Black Y=Yellow G=Green Brn=Brown

1.

W	Blu
P	W

	R	Blk
	Blk	R

love   hate

love

hate

2.

Blk
W

Blu
Y

friend   enemy

friend

enemy

3.

Blu
W
Blk
W

Y
Blu
Brn
G

city   farm

city

farm

© 1990 by Incentive Publications, Inc., Nashville, TN.

* Answer Key

COLORS AND FEELINGS II

Follow the color key below to color each figure.
Draw a line from each figure to the word that best describes it.
Then make a new figure to represent each word.

O=Orange P=Pink R=Red W=White Blu=Blue Blk=Black Y=Yellow G=Green Brn=Brown

1.

Blk
Blu

Y
W

far   near

far

near

2.

Blu   Blu
Blk

Y   Y
O

laugh   cry

laugh

cry

3.

R
O
R

G
Blu
G

talk   scream

talk

scream

© 1990 by Incentive Publications, Inc., Nashville, TN.

* Answer Key

Name _____

COLORS AND FEELINGS III

Follow the color key below to color each figure.
Draw a line from each figure to the word that best describes it.
Then make a new figure to represent each word.

O=Orange P=Pink R=Red W=White Blu=Blue Blk=Black Y=Yellow G=Green Brn=Brown

1. (G) (R) stop go	stop go
2. (Y / O) (Blu / G) happy sad	happy sad
3. (W / Blu) (Y / O) cold warm	cold warm

© 1990 by Incentive Publications, Inc., Nashville, TN.

* Answer Key

COLORS AND FEELINGS IV

Follow the color key below to color each figure.
Draw a line from each figure to the word that best describes it.
Then make a new figure to represent each word.

O=Orange P=Pink R=Red W=White Blu=Blue Blk=Black Y=Yellow G=Green Brn=Brown

1.

O

R

Y

Blu

G

Blu

rest   play

rest

play

2.

Y

Blk

day   night

day

night

3.

Blk   Blk

W

P   P

W

strange   friendly

strange

friendly

© 1990 by Incentive Publications, Inc., Nashville, TN.

* Answer Key

COLORS AND FEELINGS V

Follow the color key below to color each figure.
Draw a line from each figure to the word that best describes it.
Then make a new figure to represent each word.

O=Orange P=Pink R=Red W=White Blu=Blue Blk=Black Y=Yellow G=Green Brn=Brown

1.		
G, Blk P, W		light
light heavy		heavy
2.		
Blk, Brn Y, R		slow
slow fast		fast
3.		
Blu, Blu, Blk Blk, Blk, Y		open
open closed		closed

© 1990 by Incentive Publications, Inc., Nashville, TN.

* Answer Key

COLORS AND FEELINGS VI

Follow the color key below to color each figure.
Draw a line from each figure to the word that best describes it.
Then make a new figure to represent each word.

O=Orange P=Pink R=Red W=White Blu=Blue Blk=Black Y=Yellow G=Green Brn=Brown

1.

Blk
Brn
Blk

R
Blu
R

boring   exciting

boring

exciting

2.

Brn

G

living   not living

living

not living

3.

W
P

O
R

loud   quiet

loud

quiet

© 1990 by Incentive Publications, Inc., Nashville, TN.

* Answer Key

COLORS AND FEELINGS VII

Follow the color key below to color each figure.
Draw a line from each figure to the word that best describes it.
Then make a new figure to represent each word.

O=Orange P=Pink R=Red W=White Blu=Blue Blk=Black Y=Yellow G=Green Brn=Brown

1.

Y P Y P
P Y P Y

Blk P Blk G
R Blk O Blk

easy   hard

easy

hard

2.

P

R

mother   daughter

mother

daughter

3.

Y
G

Blk
Brn

sunny   rainy

sunny

rainy

© 1990 by Incentive Publications, Inc., Nashville, TN.

* Answer Key

COLORS AND FEELINGS VIII

Follow the color key below to color each figure.
Draw a line from each figure to the word that best describes it.
Then make a new figure to represent each word.

O=Orange P=Pink R=Red W=White Blu=Blue Blk=Black Y=Yellow G=Green Brn=Brown

1.

Blu
W

summer

Y
G

winter

summer

winter

2.

Blu
G

spring

O
Brn

fall

spring

fall

3.

R
Blk
R

mad

Y
G
Y

happy

mad

happy

© 1990 by Incentive Publications, Inc., Nashville, TN.

* Answer Key

ENRICHMENT: IMAGINATION

The Problem: Thinking about thinking.

The Activity: Reproduce and distribute pages 186-198. Instruct the students to write an appropriate phrase or draw a picture describing each character's thoughts.

PROCESS/SKILLS CHART

Complex Process
Critical Thinking
✓ **Creative Thinking**

Thought Scheme
Convergent Thinking
✓ **Divergent Thinking**

Content Skills
Reading Skills Required
Writing Skills Required
Counting Skills Required

Basic Skills
✓ **Analysis**
Categorizing
Classifying
✓ **Comparison**

Conditional Logic
Deductive Reasoning
Grouping
Hypothesizing
Identification
✓ **Imagination**
Inductive Reasoning
✓ **Inference**
✓ **Intuition**
Labeling
Logical Reasoning
✓ **Originality**
Part to Whole Relationships
Patterning
✓ **Relationships (Visual)**
Sequencing
Spatial Relationships
Synthesis
Transformations

Notes:

ENRICHMENT: IMAGINATION I

Write a phrase or draw a picture describing each character's thoughts.

© 1990 by Incentive Publications, Inc., Nashville, TN.

ENRICHMENT: IMAGINATION II

Write a phrase or draw a picture describing the character's thoughts.

© 1990 by Incentive Publications, Inc., Nashville, TN.

ENRICHMENT: IMAGINATION III

Write a phrase or draw a picture describing the character's thoughts.

© 1990 by Incentive Publications, Inc., Nashville, TN.

Name _____

ENRICHMENT: IMAGINATION IV

Write a phrase or draw a picture describing the character's thoughts.

© 1990 by Incentive Publications, Inc., Nashville, TN.

ENRICHMENT: IMAGINATION V

Write a phrase or draw a picture describing the character's thoughts.

© 1990 by Incentive Publications, Inc., Nashville, TN.

Name _____

ENRICHMENT: IMAGINATION VI

Write a phrase or draw a picture describing the character's thoughts.

© 1990 by Incentive Publications, Inc., Nashville, TN.

ENRICHMENT: IMAGINATION VII

Write a phrase or draw a picture describing the character's thoughts.

© 1990 by Incentive Publications, Inc., Nashville, TN.

ENRICHMENT: IMAGINATION VIII

Write a phrase or draw a picture describing each character's thoughts.

© 1990 by Incentive Publications, Inc., Nashville, TN.

ENRICHMENT: IMAGINATION IX

Write a phrase or draw a picture describing each character's thoughts.

© 1990 by Incentive Publications, Inc., Nashville, TN.

ENRICHMENT: IMAGINATION X

Write a phrase or draw a picture describing the character's thoughts.

© 1990 by Incentive Publications, Inc., Nashville, TN.

ENRICHMENT: IMAGINATION XI

Write a phrase or draw a picture describing the character's thoughts.

© 1990 by Incentive Publications, Inc., Nashville, TN.

ENRICHMENT: IMAGINATION XII

Write a phrase or draw a picture describing each character's thoughts.

© 1990 by Incentive Publications, Inc., Nashville, TN.

Name _____

ENRICHMENT: IMAGINATION XIII

Write a phrase or draw a picture describing each character's thoughts.

© 1990 by Incentive Publications, Inc., Nashville, TN.

SPACE AND PLACE:
STAR CHART

The Problem: Spatial and proportional placement of several figures (including overlapping).

The Activity: Reproduce and distribute pages 200 and 201. Instruct the students to draw each of the six satellites and stars on the star chart, being sure to place each figure proportionately to its original position and size. (There will be overlapping if done properly.)

PROCESS/SKILLS CHART

Complex Process
   Critical Thinking
   ✓ **Creative Thinking**

Thought Scheme
   Convergent Thinking
   ✓ **Divergent Thinking**

Content Skills
   Reading Skills Required
   Writing Skills Required
   Counting Skills Required

Basic Skills
   ✓ **Analysis**
   Categorizing
   Classifying
   ✓ **Comparison**

✓ **Conditional Logic**
✓ **Deductive Reasoning**
   Grouping
   Hypothesizing
   Identification
✓ **Imagination**
   Inductive Reasoning
   Inference
   Intuition
   Labeling
✓ **Logical Reasoning**
   Originality
✓ **Part to Whole Relationships**
   Patterning
   Relationships (Visual)
   Sequencing
✓ **Spatial Relationships**
✓ **Synthesis**
✓ **Transformations**

Notes:

Name _____

SPACE AND PLACE: STAR CHART I

Draw each of these six satellites and stars in the star chart below.

Be sure to place each figure proportionately to its original position and size.

There will be overlapping if done properly.

STAR CHART

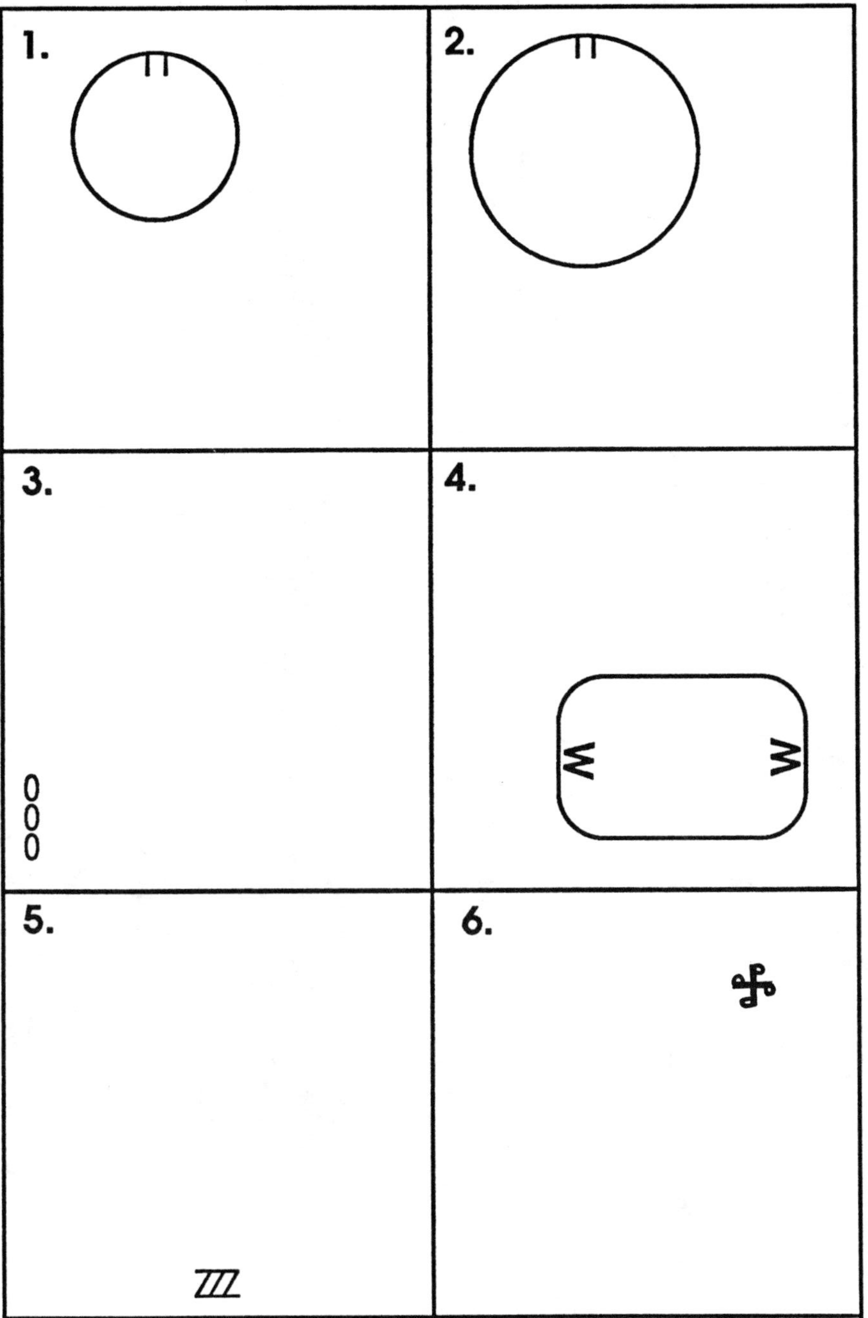

1.

2.

3.

4.

5.

6.

SATELLITES AND STARS

© 1990 by Incentive Publications, Inc., Nashville, TN.

*Answer Key

SPACE AND PLACE:
STAR CHART II

Draw each of these six satellites and stars in the star chart below.

Be sure to place each figure proportionately to its original position and size.

There will be overlapping if done properly.

STAR CHART

1.

2.

3.

4.

5.

6.

SATELLITES AND STARS

© 1990 by Incentive Publications, Inc., Nashville, TN.

*Answer Key

SPACE AND PLACE: REVERSED STAR CHART

The Problem: Spatial and proportional placement of several figures (reduction in size).

The Activity: Reproduce and distribute pages 203-205. Instruct the students to draw each figure in the correct numbered box, being sure to place it proportionately according to its size and position in the star chart.

PROCESS/SKILLS CHART

Complex Process
- ✓ Critical Thinking
- ✓ Creative Thinking

Thought Scheme
- ✓ Convergent Thinking
- Divergent Thinking

Content Skills
- Reading Skills Required
- Writing Skills Required
- Counting Skills Required

Basic Skills
- ✓ Analysis
- Categorizing
- Classifying
- ✓ Comparison

- ✓ Conditional Logic
- ✓ Deductive Reasoning
- Grouping
- Hypothesizing
- Identification
- ✓ Imagination
- Inductive Reasoning
- Inference
- Intuition
- Labeling
- Logical Reasoning
- Originality
- ✓ Part to Whole Relationships
- Patterning
- Relationships (Visual)
- Sequencing
- ✓ Spatial Relationships
- ✓ Synthesis
- ✓ Transformations

Notes:

Name _____

SPACE AND PLACE:
REVERSED STAR CHART I

Draw each figure in the correct numbered box.
Be sure to place each figure proportionately
according to its size and position in the star chart.

STAR CHART

1.	2.
3.	4.
5.	6.

SATELLITES AND STARS

© 1990 by Incentive Publications, Inc., Nashville, TN.

*Answer Key

*Answer Key

SATELLITES AND STARS

2.	1.
4.	3.
6.	5.

Name _____

SPACE AND PLACE:
REVERSED STAR CHART II

Draw each figure in the correct numbered box.
Be sure to place each figure proportionately
according to its size and position in the star chart.

STAR CHART

© 1990 by Incentive Publications, Inc., Nashville, TN.

204

SPACE AND PLACE:
REVERSED STAR CHART III

Draw each figure in the correct numbered box.
Be sure to place each figure proportionately
according to its size and position in the star chart.

STAR CHART

1.	2.
3.	4.
5.	6.

SATELLITES AND STARS

© 1990 by Incentive Publications, Inc., Nashville, TN.

*Answer Key

GRID ENLARGING

The Problem: Using visual clues to proportionately increase the size of a figure.

The Activity: Reproduce and distribute pages 207-210. Instruct the students to enlarge each figure by drawing it on the large grid with the corresponding number. Remind the students to keep each figure in the proper proportion.

Enrichment: These figures and/or original designs can be enlarged on graph paper of various sizes or can be made into mural size by drawing the grids on butcher paper. The figures also can be accurately reduced using the same method.

PROCESS/SKILLS CHART

Complex Process
- ✓ **Critical Thinking**
- Creative Thinking

Thought Scheme
- ✓ **Convergent Thinking**
- Divergent Thinking

Content Skills
- Reading Skills Required
- Writing Skills Required
- Counting Skills Required

Basic Skills
- ✓ **Analysis**
- Categorizing
- Classifying
- ✓ **Comparison**

- ✓ **Conditional Logic**
- ✓ **Deductive Reasoning**
- Grouping
- Hypothesizing
- Identification
- ✓ **Imagination**
- Inductive Reasoning
- Inference
- Intuition
- Labeling
- Logical Reasoning
- Originality
- ✓ **Part to Whole Relationships**
- Patterning
- ✓ **Relationships (Visual)**
- ✓ **Sequencing**
- ✓ **Spatial Relationships**
- ✓ **Synthesis**
- ✓ **Transformations**

Notes:

Name _____

GRID ENLARGING I

Enlarge each figure by drawing it on the large grid with the corresponding number.
Try to keep each figure in the proper proportion.

1

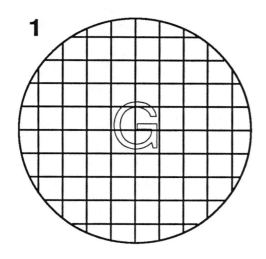

2

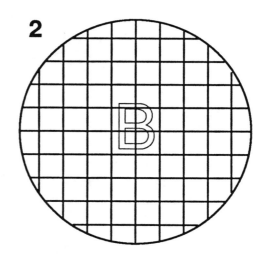

1

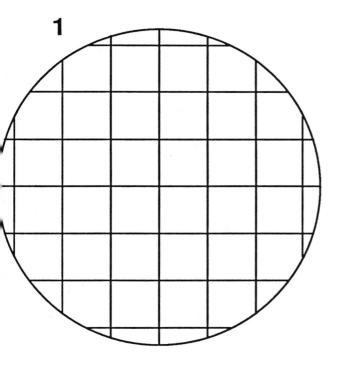

2

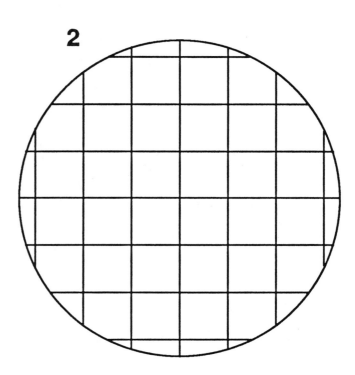

© 1990 by Incentive Publications, Inc., Nashville, TN.

Name _____

GRID ENLARGING II

Enlarge each figure by drawing it on the large grid with the corresponding number.
Try to keep each figure in the proper proportion.

1

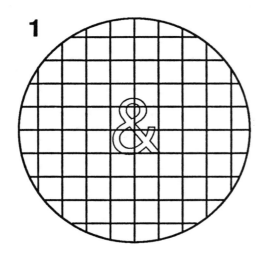

2

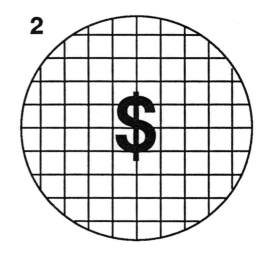

1

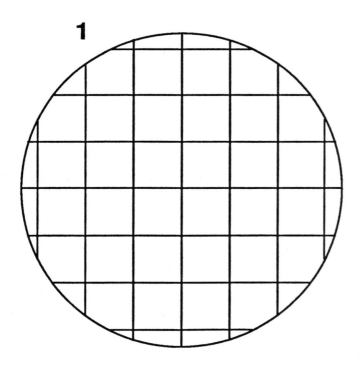

2

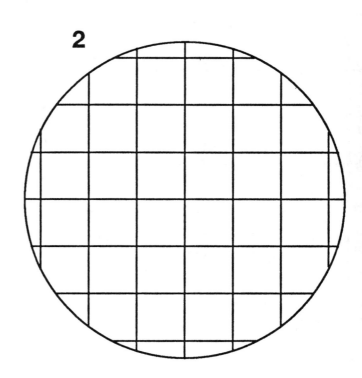

© 1990 by Incentive Publications, Inc., Nashville, TN.

GRID ENLARGING III

Enlarge each figure by drawing it on the large grid with the corresponding number.
Try to keep each figure in the proper proportion.

1
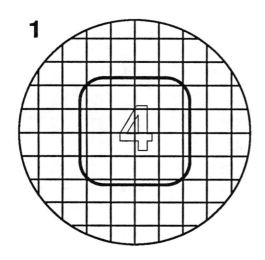

2
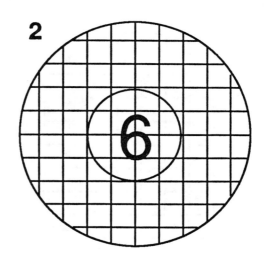

1
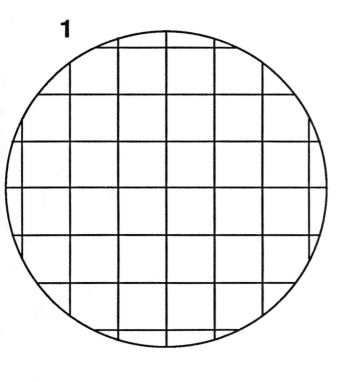

2
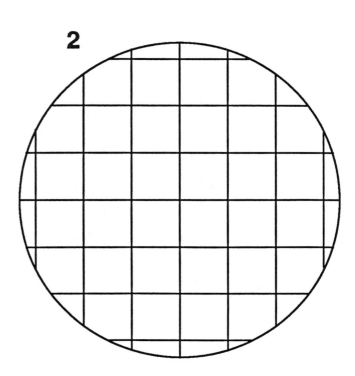

© 1990 by Incentive Publications, Inc., Nashville, TN.

Name _____

GRID ENLARGING IV

Draw your own figures in the small grids.
Then enlarge the figures by drawing them in the large grids with the
 corresponding numbers.
Try to keep each figure in the proper proportion.

1
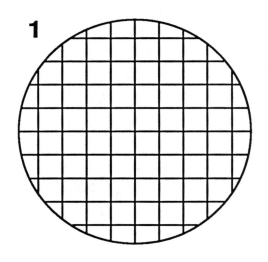

2
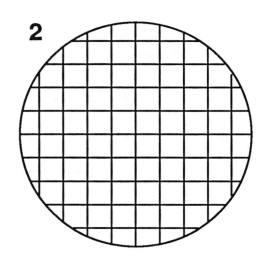

1
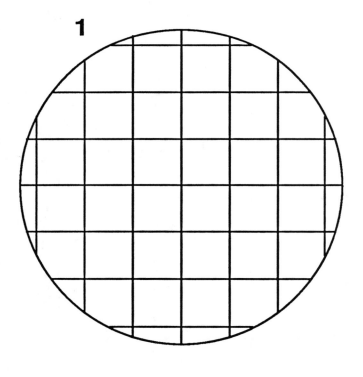

2
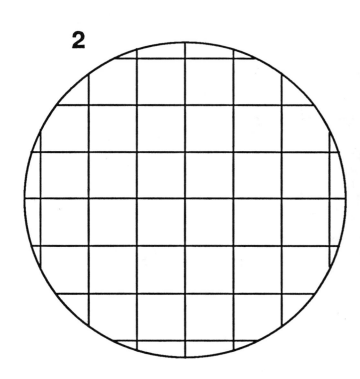

© 1990 by Incentive Publications, Inc., Nashville, TN.

GRID ENLARGING: DISTORTION PROPORTION

The Problem: Proportionately enlarging and/or reducing a figure on a distorted grid.

The Activity: Reproduce and distribute page 212. Instruct the students to transfer several figures from pages 207-210 onto the distorted grid.

Enrichment: Have the students place the same figures in different areas of the grid and note their changes.

PROCESS/SKILLS CHART

Complex Process
- ✓ Critical Thinking
- Creative Thinking

Thought Scheme
- ✓ Convergent Thinking
- Divergent Thinking

Content Skills
- Reading Skills Required
- Writing Skills Required
- Counting Skills Required

Basic Skills
- ✓ Analysis
- Categorizing
- Classifying
- ✓ Comparison

- ✓ Conditional Logic
- ✓ Deductive Reasoning
- Grouping
- Hypothesizing
- Identification
- ✓ Imagination
- Inductive Reasoning
- Inference
- Intuition
- Labeling
- Logical Reasoning
- Originality
- ✓ Part to Whole Relationships
- Patterning
- ✓ Relationships (Visual)
- ✓ Sequencing
- ✓ Spatial Relationships
- ✓ Synthesis
- ✓ Transformations

Notes:

GRID ENLARGING: DISTORTION PROPORTION

Transfer several figures from pages 207-210 onto the distorted grid below.
Try to keep the figures in the proper proportions.

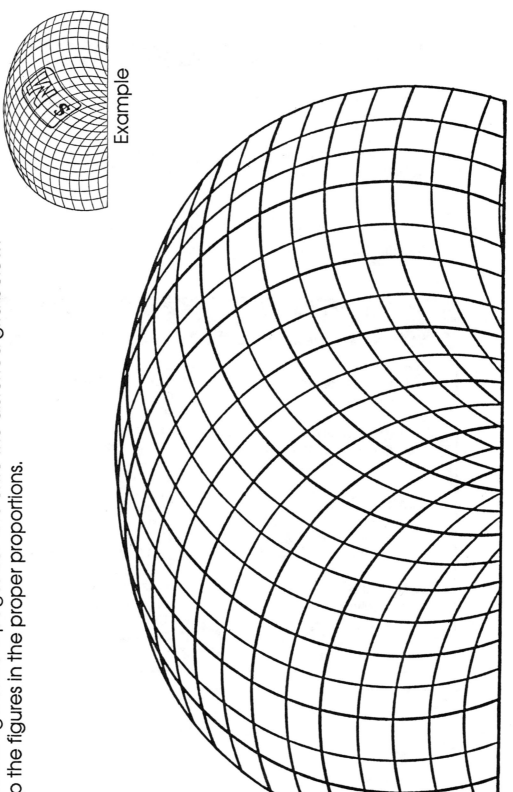

Example

© 1990 by Incentive Publications, Inc., Nashville, TN.

OP ART: TWO DIMENSIONAL

The Problem: Using visual clues and logical reasoning to answer questions and/or complete patterns and puzzles involving complex optical designs.

The Activity: Reproduce and distribute pages 214-219. Instruct the students to complete each activity as directed.

PROCESS/SKILLS CHART

Complex Process
- ✓ Critical Thinking
- ✓ Creative Thinking

Thought Scheme
- ✓ Convergent Thinking
- Divergent Thinking

Content Skills
- Reading Skills Required
- Writing Skills Required
- Counting Skills Required

Basic Skills
- ✓ Analysis
- Categorizing
- Classifying
- ✓ Comparison

- ✓ Conditional Logic
- ✓ Deductive Reasoning
- ✓ Grouping
- Hypothesizing
- ✓ Identification
- ✓ Imagination
- Inductive Reasoning
- ✓ Inference
- Intuition
- Labeling
- ✓ Logical Reasoning
- Originality
- ✓ Part to Whole Relationships
- ✓ Patterning
- ✓ Relationships (Visual)
- ✓ Sequencing
- ✓ Spatial Relationships
- ✓ Synthesis
- ✓ Transformations

Notes:

Name _____

OP ART: TWO DIMENSIONAL I

Color the squares blue.
How many squares did you find? _____
Color the triangles red.
How many triangles did you find? _____

How many circles can you find? _____

© 1990 by Incentive Publications, Inc., Nashville, TN.
Design from *Op Art Coloring Book* by Jean Larcher, © 1975 by Dover Publication, Inc.

* Answer Key

OP ART: TWO DIMENSIONAL II

Cut out the design below and glue it on another sheet of paper.
Then cut out the design pieces and glue them together on the same sheet
of paper to make an identical design.

© 1990 by Incentive Publications, Inc., Nashville, TN.

* Answer Key

OP ART:TWO DIMENSIONAL III

Cut out the design to the left of the page and glue it on another sheet of paper. Then cut out the design pieces and glue them together on the same sheet of paper to make an identical design.

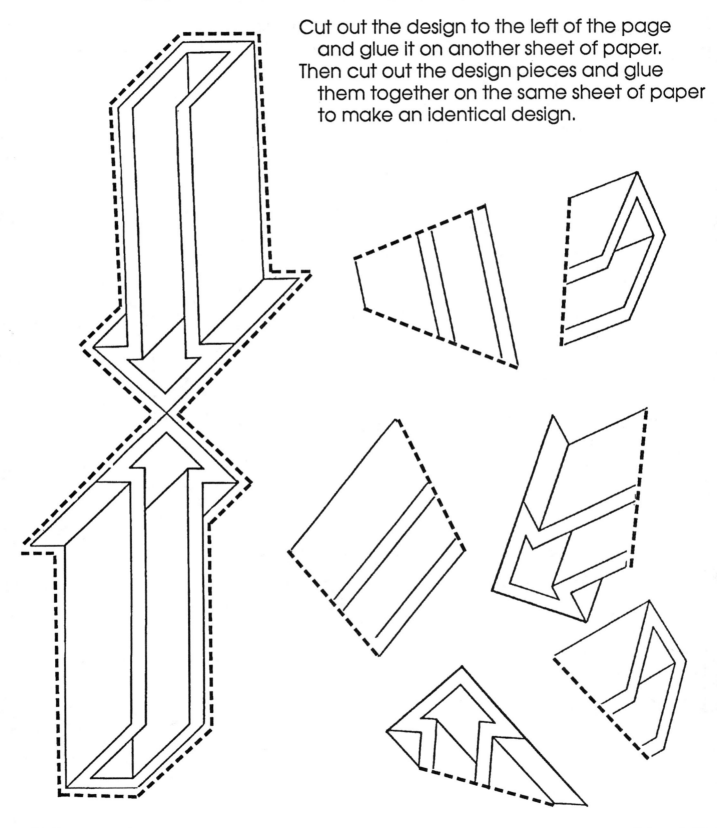

© 1990 by Incentive Publications, Inc., Nashville, TN.

* Answer Key

OP ART:
TWO DIMENSIONAL IV

Cut out the design to the left of the page and glue it on another sheet of paper.
Then cut out the design pieces and glue them together on the same sheet of paper to make an identical design.

© 1990 by Incentive Publications, Inc., Nashville, TN.

* Answer Key

Name _____

OP ART: TWO DIMENSIONAL V

Find the seven "holes" in the design and complete the design.
One is done for you.

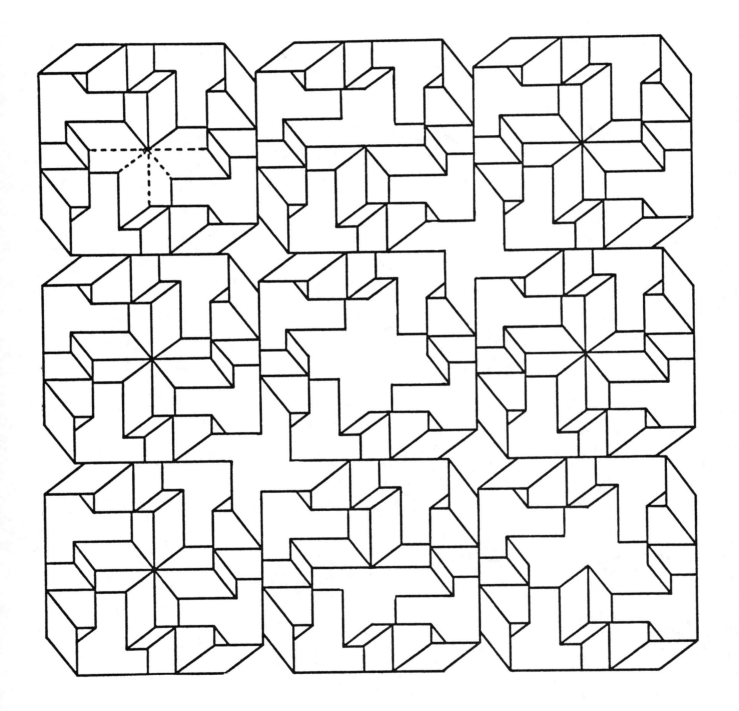

© 1990 by Incentive Publications, Inc., Nashville, TN.

* Answer Key

Name _____

OP ART: TWO DIMENSIONAL VI

Finish each design so that it looks exactly like its partner.

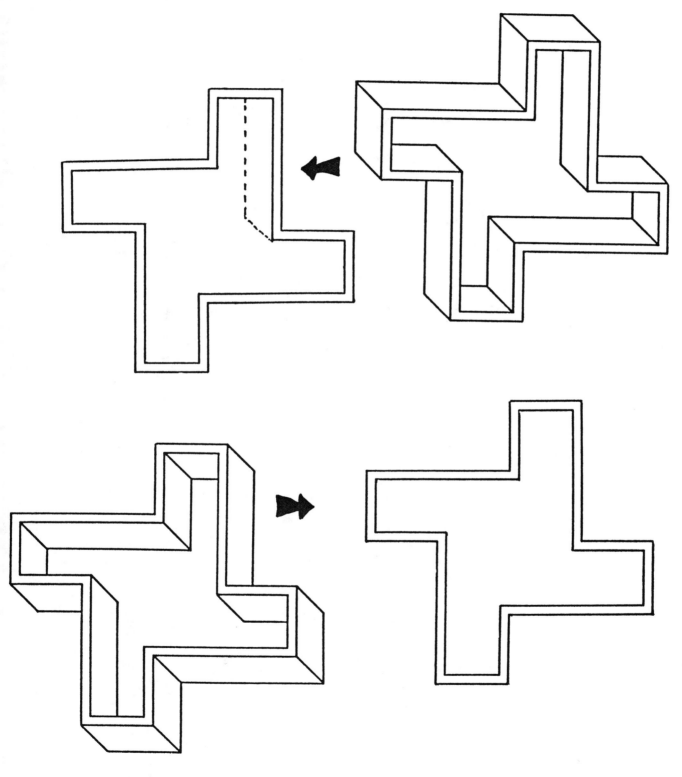

* Answer Key

APPENDIX

TEACHER'S GUIDE TO IMPROVING THINKING

The following are general suggestions for improving students' thinking skills and fostering an open classroom climate for thinking.

1. Ask open questions that leave room for divergent responses.

2. Give students "think" time before asking for responses.

3. Use clarification and expansion techniques in response to students' suggestions.

4. Be prepared with clean lesson plans.

5. Promote metacognition – thinking about thinking.

6. Be a model of "thinking" in all areas of student contact.

7. Encourage students to formulate their own questions.

8. Listen to students and encourage them to listen to each other.

9. Use cooperative learning.

10. Be accepting of divergent responses (if valid).

11. Act as a facilitator rather than an evaluator.

12. Be a model of organization and encourage students to be organized.

13. Seek justification of students' responses.

14. Encourage students to consider and explore others' points of view.

15. Provide visual clues whenever possible.

16. Use "if/then" language.

17. Whenever possible, encourage the transfer of cognitive and creative skills to everyday life.

THINKING EVALUATION

Although thought processing is a very private matter, there are obvious traits that are observable.

To evaluate a student's thinking capabilities, circle the appropriate rating for each trait described below. The numeral 1 represents an immature thinker; the numeral 5 represents a mature thinker.

Student's name: _____

Immature Thinker		Mature Thinker
1. Does not set goals.	1 2 3 4 5	Sets goals.
2. Gives up easily.	1 2 3 4 5	Works toward goal with persistence.
3. Tries only one approach toward goal.	1 2 3 4 5	Looks for alternate paths toward goal.
4. When goal cannot be met, does not modify goal.	1 2 3 4 5	When goal cannot be met, modifies goal.
5. Does not enjoy problem-solving.	1 2 3 4 5	Enjoys problem-solving.
6. Is upset by ambiguity.	1 2 3 4 5	Takes ambiguity in stride.
7. Is not able to evaluate his/her progress.	1 2 3 4 5	Is able to evaluate his/her progress.
8. Ignores suggestions of others.	1 2 3 4 5	Considers suggestions of others.
9. Needs constant prodding and interaction.	1 2 3 4 5	Spends time in quiet deliberation.
10. Investigates only the obvious.	1 2 3 4 5	Considers all evidence and actively seeks out new evidence.
11. Cannot or will not defend the value of thinking.	1 2 3 4 5	Can verbalize the value of thinking.

© 1990 by Incentive Publications, Inc., Nashville, TN.

GLOSSARY

Analogy (figural) - a problem-solving strategy in which figural similarities are noted between two or more examples and differences in the relationship are realized

Analyze - to separate a whole into parts according to some reason

Categorize - to arrange items so that each has characteristics required for that group

Classify - to sort into groups according to common characteristics and to label each group accordingly

Cognition - various human thinking processes

Conditional Logic - logical statements that are expressed in an "if/then" format

Convergent Thinking - thinking that requires one correct answer

Creative Thinking - being able to produce along novel and/or original lines

Critical Thinking - using basic thinking processes to analyze problems

Deductive Reasoning - to infer from what precedes or to use clues to come to a conclusion

Divergent Thinking - thinking that generates many responses to the same problem

Evaluation - to make a judgment based on internal or external criteria

Hypothesis - an assumption that serves as a basis for investigation

Identify (structural) - to describe relationships among the parts of a pattern, figure or design

Inductive Reasoning - forming a conclusion by inference of different facts and/or assumptions

Infer - to reach a tentative conclusion that evidence points toward but does not absolutely prove ("supposition that leads to prediction")

Intuition - reaching knowledge without critical thinking or inference

Label - to assign a name to a group of related figures, objects or ideas (the name must refer to a basic characteristic of the members of the group)

Logical Reasoning - to think in a systematic fashion in order to reach a conclusion

Metacognition - being aware of one's own thinking processes

Originality - generating novel responses or products

Part to Whole Relationships - understanding how the individual elements of a situation or design combine to form a complete unit

Patterning - arranging a series of objects, figures or situations according to a set plan

Problem-solving - to define a problem, determine the desired outcome, infer possible solutions or strategies, test ideas and evaluate the outcome

Relationships - finding "likenesses" and/or "differences" between objects, figures or ideas

Sequence - arranging items in an order according to some relationship

Synthesize - using hypothesized ideas in application

Thinking - formulating thoughts through mental manipulation of sensory input

Transformations - relating known to unknown characteristics and creating meanings

ANSWER KEY

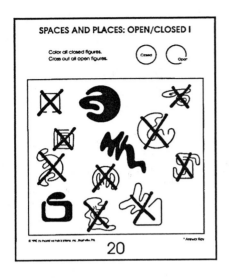

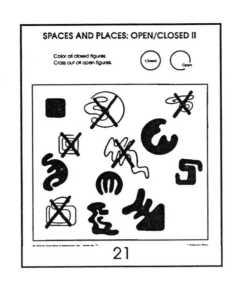

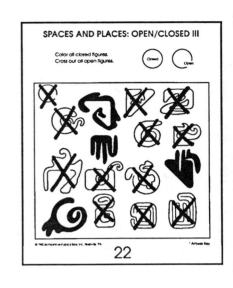

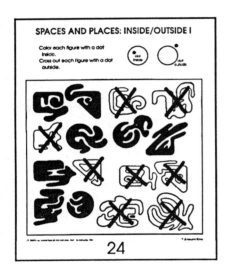

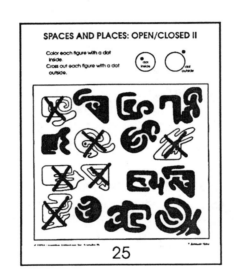

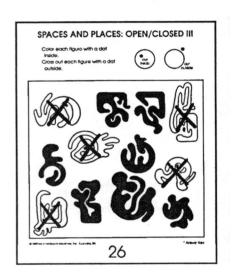

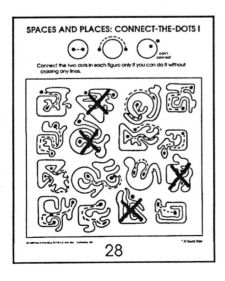

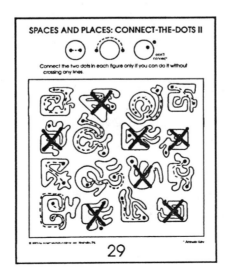

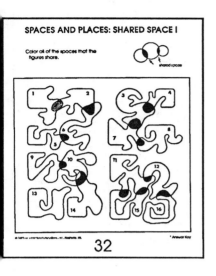

SPACES AND PLACES: SHARED SPACE I

Color all of the spaces that the figures share.

32

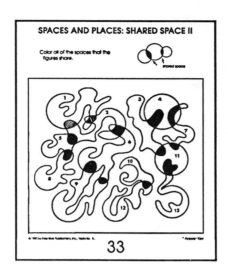

SPACES AND PLACES: SHARED SPACE II

Color all of the spaces that the figures share.

33

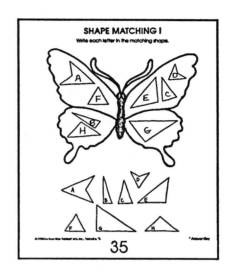

SHAPE MATCHING I

Write each letter in the matching shape.

35

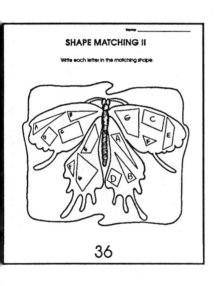

SHAPE MATCHING II

Write each letter in the matching shape.

36

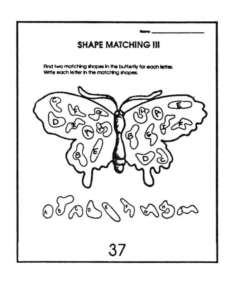

SHAPE MATCHING III

Find two matching shapes in the butterfly for each letter.
Write each letter in the matching shapes.

37

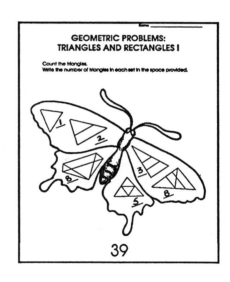

GEOMETRIC PROBLEMS:
TRIANGLES AND RECTANGLES I

Count the triangles.
Write the number of triangles in each set in the space provided.

39

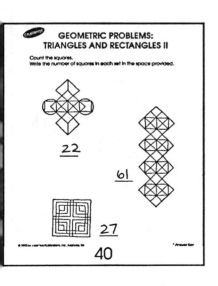

GEOMETRIC PROBLEMS:
TRIANGLES AND RECTANGLES II

Count the squares.
Write the number of squares in each set in the space provided.

40

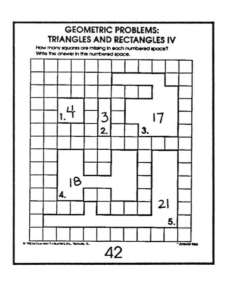

GEOMETRIC PROBLEMS:
TRIANGLES AND RECTANGLES IV

How many squares are missing in each numbered space?
Write the answer in the numbered space.

42

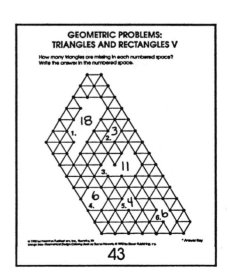

GEOMETRIC PROBLEMS:
TRIANGLES AND RECTANGLES V

How many triangles are missing in each numbered space?
Write the answer in the numbered space.

43

227

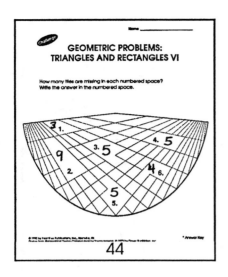

GEOMETRIC PROBLEMS: TRIANGLES AND RECTANGLES VI

How many tiles are missing in each numbered space?
Write the answer in the numbered space.

44

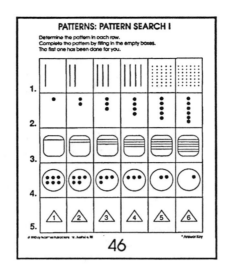

PATTERNS: PATTERN SEARCH I

Determine the pattern in each row.
Complete the pattern by filling in the empty boxes.
The first one has been done for you.

46

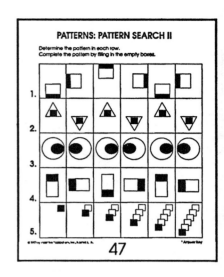

PATTERNS: PATTERN SEARCH II

Determine the pattern in each row.
Complete the pattern by filling in the empty boxes.

47

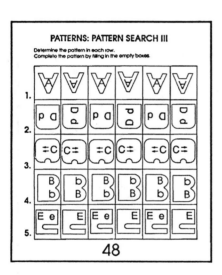

PATTERNS: PATTERN SEARCH III

Determine the pattern in each row.
Complete the pattern by filling in the empty boxes.

48

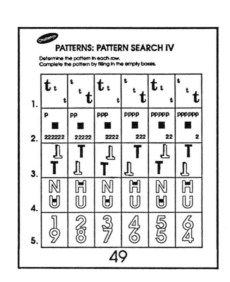

PATTERNS: PATTERN SEARCH IV

Determine the pattern in each row.
Complete the pattern by filling in the empty boxes.

49

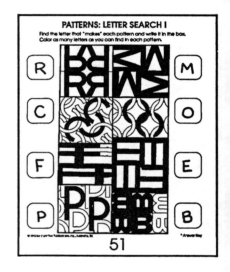

PATTERNS: LETTER SEARCH I

Find the letter that "makes" each pattern and write it in the box.
Color as many letters as you can find in each pattern.

51

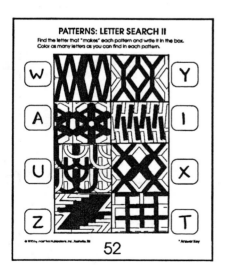

PATTERNS: LETTER SEARCH II

Find the letter that "makes" each pattern and write it in the box.
Color as many letters as you can find in each pattern.

52

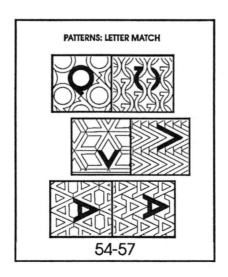

PATTERNS: LETTER MATCH

54-57

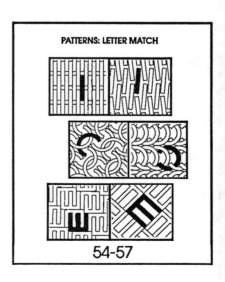

PATTERNS: LETTER MATCH

54-57

228

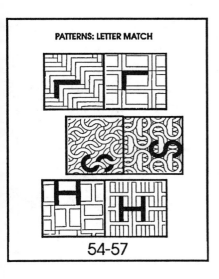

PATTERNS: LETTER MATCH

54-57

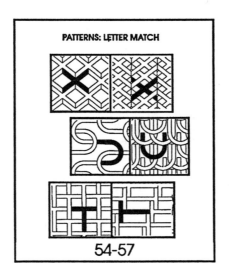

PATTERNS: LETTER MATCH

54-57

PUZZLES: ALPHA-MYSTERY I

Determine what letter is in the pattern pieces below.
Color at least one letter.
Cut out the pattern pieces and assemble them to form the letter.

59

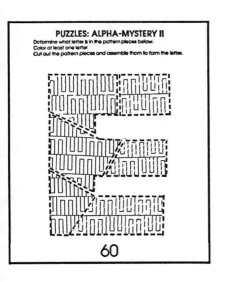

PUZZLES: ALPHA-MYSTERY II

Determine what letter is in the pattern pieces below.
Color at least one letter.
Cut out the pattern pieces and assemble them to form the letter.

60

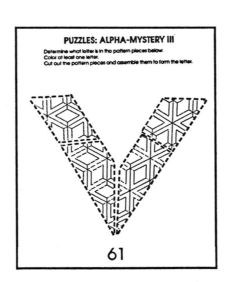

PUZZLES: ALPHA-MYSTERY III

Determine what letter is in the pattern pieces below.
Color at least one letter.
Cut out the pattern pieces and assemble them to form the letter.

61

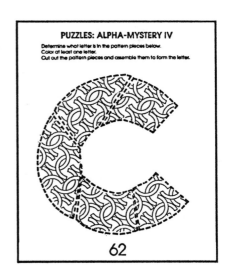

PUZZLES: ALPHA-MYSTERY IV

Determine what letter is in the pattern pieces below.
Color at least one letter.
Cut out the pattern pieces and assemble them to form the letter.

62

PUZZLES: ALPHA-MYSTERY V

Determine what letter is in the pattern pieces below.
Color at least one letter.
Cut out the pattern pieces and assemble them to form the letter.

63

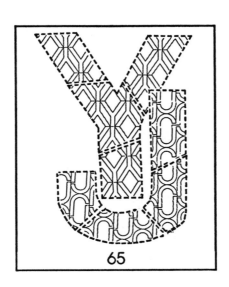

65

66

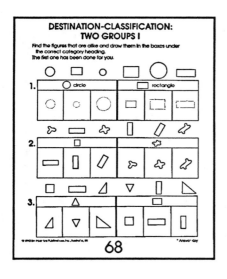

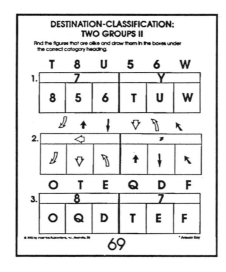

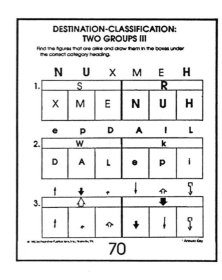

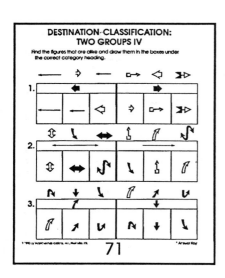

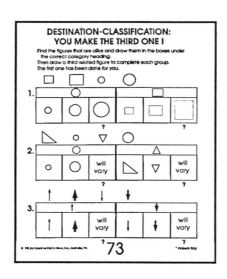

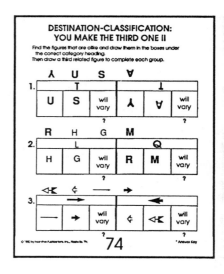

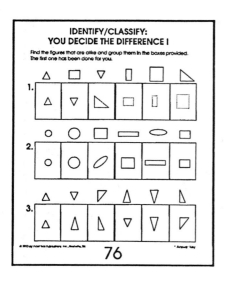

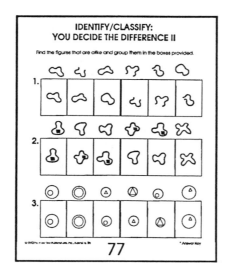

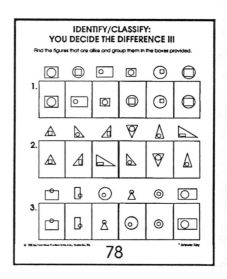

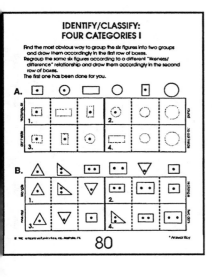

IDENTIFY/CLASSIFY:
FOUR CATEGORIES I

Find the most obvious way to group the six figures into two groups and draw them accordingly in the first row of boxes.
Regroup the same six figures according to a different "likeness/difference" relationship and draw them accordingly in the second row of boxes.
The first one has been done for you.

80

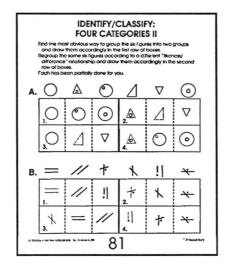

IDENTIFY/CLASSIFY:
FOUR CATEGORIES II

Find the most obvious way to group the six figures into two groups and draw them accordingly in the first row of boxes.
Regroup the same six figures according to a different "likeness/difference" relationship and draw them accordingly in the second row of boxes.
Each has been partially done for you.

81

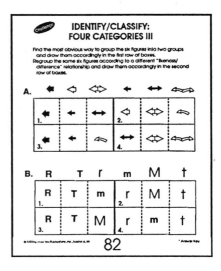

IDENTIFY/CLASSIFY:
FOUR CATEGORIES III

Find the most obvious way to group the six figures into two groups and draw them accordingly in the first row of boxes.
Regroup the same six figures according to a different "likeness/difference" relationship and draw them accordingly in the second row of boxes.

82

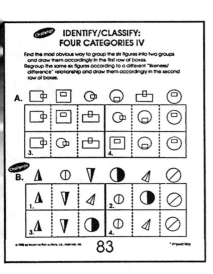

IDENTIFY/CLASSIFY:
FOUR CATEGORIES IV

Find the most obvious way to group the six figures into two groups and draw them accordingly in the first row of boxes.
Regroup the same six figures according to a different "likeness/difference" relationship and draw them accordingly in the second row of boxes.

83

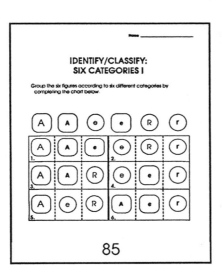

IDENTIFY/CLASSIFY:
SIX CATEGORIES I

Group the six figures according to six different categories by completing the chart below.

85

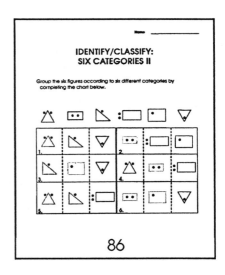

IDENTIFY/CLASSIFY:
SIX CATEGORIES II

Group the six figures according to six different categories by completing the chart below.

86

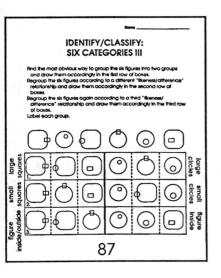

IDENTIFY/CLASSIFY:
SIX CATEGORIES III

Find the most obvious way to group the six figures into two groups and draw them accordingly in the first row of boxes.
Regroup the six figures according to a different "likeness/difference" relationship and draw them accordingly in the second row of boxes.
Regroup the six figures again according to a third "likeness/difference" relationship and draw them accordingly in the third row of boxes.
Label each group.

87

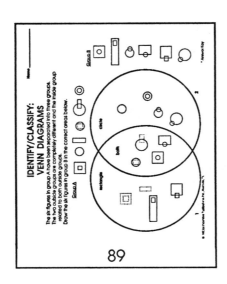

IDENTIFY/CLASSIFY:
VENN DIAGRAMS

The six figures in group A have been separated into three groups.
The two outside groups are completely different and the inside group is related to both outside groups.
Draw the six figures in group B in the correct areas below.

89

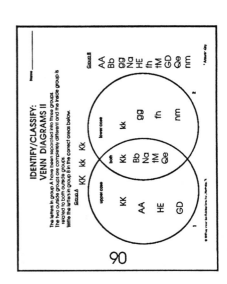

IDENTIFY/CLASSIFY:
VENN DIAGRAMS II

The letters in group A have been separated into three groups.
The two outside groups are completely different and the inside group is related to both outside groups.
Write the letters in group B in the correct areas below.

90

231

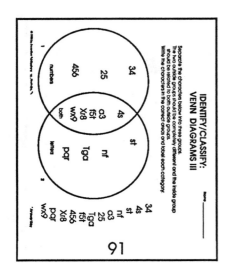

IDENTIFY/CLASSIFY: VENN DIAGRAMS III

91

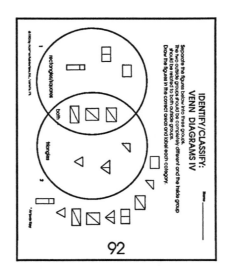

IDENTIFY/CLASSIFY: VENN DIAGRAMS IV

92

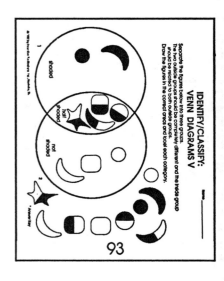

IDENTIFY/CLASSIFY: VENN DIAGRAMS V

93

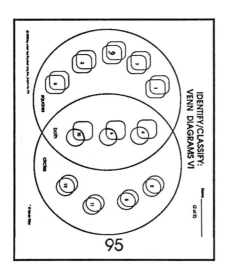

IDENTIFY/CLASSIFY: VENN DIAGRAMS VI

95

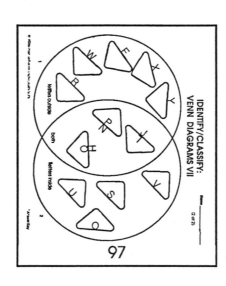

IDENTIFY/CLASSIFY: VENN DIAGRAMS VII

97

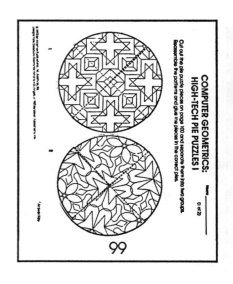

COMPUTER GEOMETRICS: HIGH-TECH PIE PUZZLES I

99

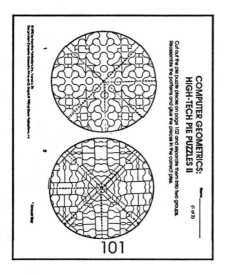

COMPUTER GEOMETRICS: HIGH-TECH PIE PUZZLES II

101

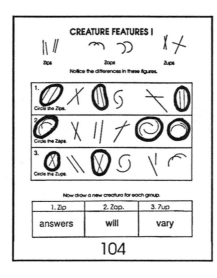

CREATURE FEATURES I

1. Zip	2. Zap.	3. 7up
answers	will	vary

104

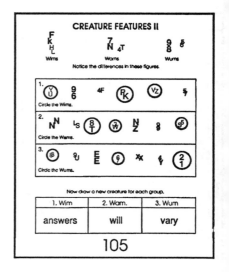

CREATURE FEATURES II

1. Wim	2. Wam.	3. Wum
answers	will	vary

105

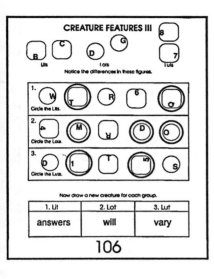

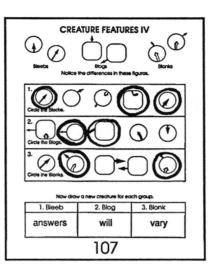

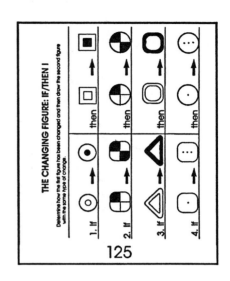

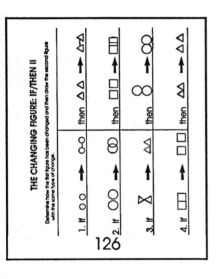

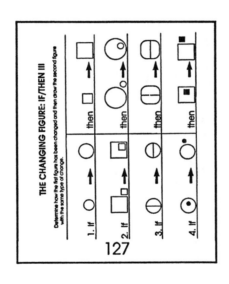

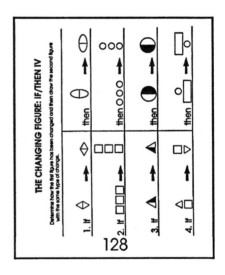

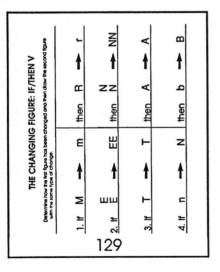

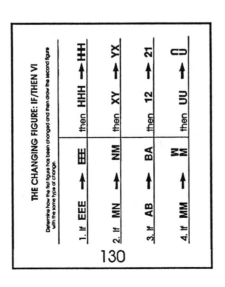

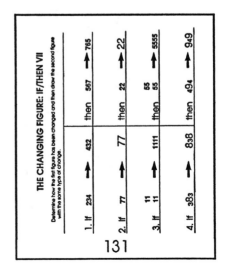

233

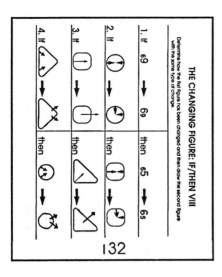

THE CHANGING FIGURE: IF/THEN VIII

Determine how the first figure has been changed and then draw the second figure with the same type of change.

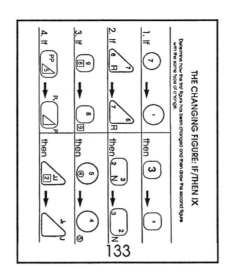

THE CHANGING FIGURE: IF/THEN IX

Determine how the first figure has been changed and then draw the second figure with the same type of change.

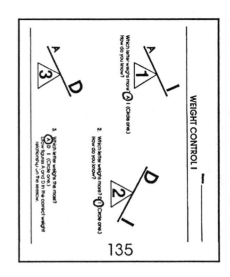

WEIGHT CONTROL I

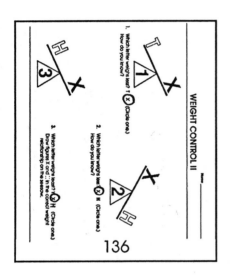

WEIGHT CONTROL II

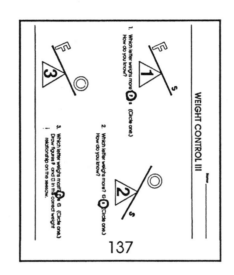

WEIGHT CONTROL III

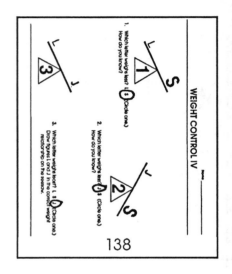

WEIGHT CONTROL IV

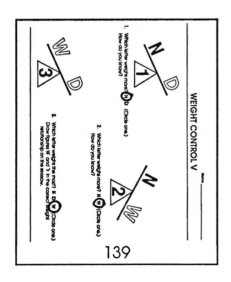

WEIGHT CONTROL V

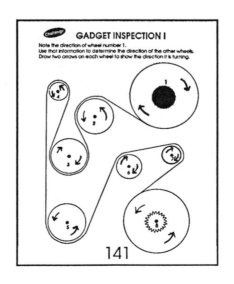

GADGET INSPECTION I

Note the direction of wheel number 1.
Use that information to determine the direction of the other wheels.
Draw two arrows on each wheel to show the direction it is turning.

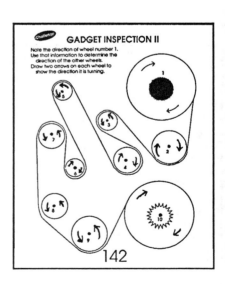

GADGET INSPECTION II

Note the direction of wheel number 1.
Use that information to determine the direction of the other wheels.
Draw two arrows on each wheel to show the direction it is turning.

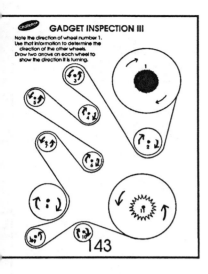

GADGET INSPECTION III

Note the direction of wheel number 1.
Use that information to determine the direction of the other wheels.
Draw two arrows on each wheel to show the direction it is turning.

143

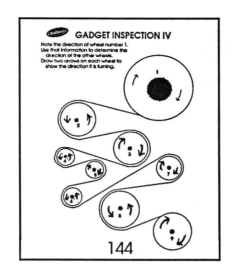

GADGET INSPECTION IV

Note the direction of wheel number 1.
Use that information to determine the direction of the other wheels.
Draw two arrows on each wheel to show the direction it is turning.

144

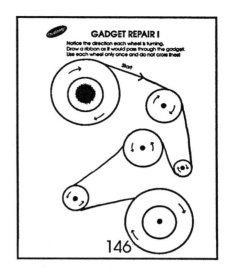

GADGET REPAIR I

Notice the direction each wheel is turning.
Draw a ribbon as it would pass through the gadget.
Use each wheel only once and do not cross lines!

146

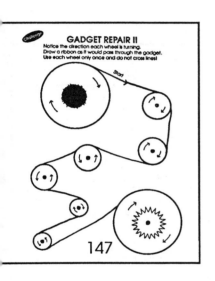

GADGET REPAIR II

Notice the direction each wheel is turning.
Draw a ribbon as it would pass through the gadget.
Use each wheel only once and do not cross lines!

147

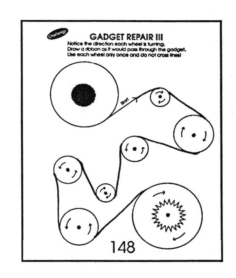

GADGET REPAIR III

Notice the direction each wheel is turning.
Draw a ribbon as it would pass through the gadget.
Use each wheel only once and do not cross lines!

148

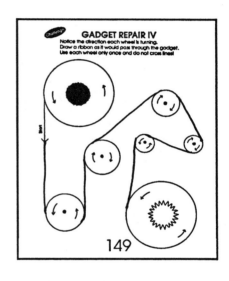

GADGET REPAIR IV

Notice the direction each wheel is turning.
Draw a ribbon as it would pass through the gadget.
Use each wheel only once and do not cross lines!

149

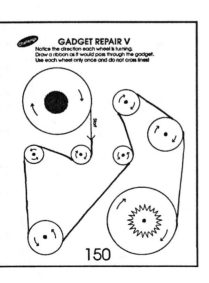

GADGET REPAIR V

Notice the direction each wheel is turning.
Draw a ribbon as it would pass through the gadget.
Use each wheel only once and do not cross lines!

150

	Pg 152		
A.	1. Too	2. Boo	3. Doo
B.	1. Koo	2. Loo	3. Goo

	Pg 153		
A.	1. B12	2. V8	3. BD2
B.	1. Wv2	2. Kkt	3. Tp3

Pg 154		
1. 88	2. 7	3. 999
4. Xxx	5. Yy	6. z

Pg 155		
1. FXi	2. SIP	3. BLIP
4. KIP	5. PIP	

152-155

Pg 156		
1. Y9	2. Q92	3. ZP7
4. Voo	5. Doo	

Pg 157		
1. We6	2. IM9	3. PU
4. 4U	5. UR8	

Pg 158		
1. Koo	2. Su8	3. Soo
4. Eoo	5. Nu9	6. Xoo
7. Bu2		

Pg 159				
1. 3P	2. 6F	3. 7Z	4. 9C	5. 8S

Pg 160				
1. L6	2. P8	3. M9	4. T7	5. R10

156-160

Pg 162
1. a. 6
   b. 9, 2
   c. 4, 3
   d. 4, 6, 3

2. a. F C E L
   b. A C E H
   c. C E
   d. N P W Z
   e. N A P W H Z

Pg 163
1. a. A, W, X, S, Q, U   2. a. 7 only
   b. D, A, E, K, W, O, X   b. 7 only
   c. W, X, K, O   c. none
   d. A, W, X   d. 4, 5, O
   e. W, X   e. 6 only

162-163

Pg 164
1. a. G only   2. a. 1, 2, 0, 8, 15
   b. S only   b. 7 only
   c. O only   c. 6 only
   d. none   d. none
   e. H only   e. 2, 0, 15
   f. F, T, V

Pg 165
1. a. V, A, X, S,   2. a. 2, 1, 10, 3,
      L, Y, T, R   14, 4, 5, 13
   b. S only   6, 7, 8, 15,
   c. A, S, T   12, 16, 0
   d. V, A, X   b. 1, 2, 16, 0,
   e. E, G   12, 9
                     c. none
                     d. 0 only
                     e. 2, 10, 5, 4,
                        13, 15, 6, 8,
164-165 16, 12, 9

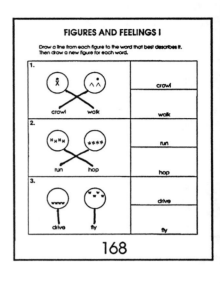

FIGURES AND FEELINGS I

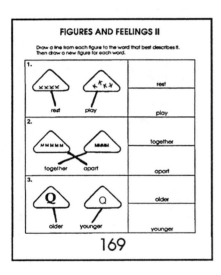

FIGURES AND FEELINGS II

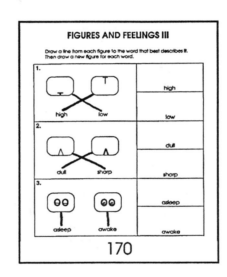

FIGURES AND FEELINGS III

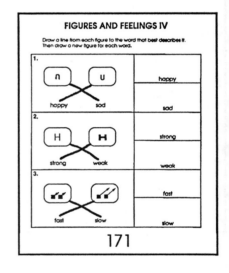

FIGURES AND FEELINGS IV

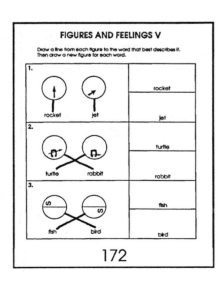

FIGURES AND FEELINGS V

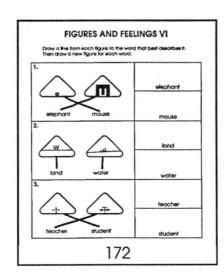

FIGURES AND FEELINGS VI

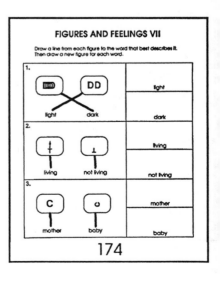

FIGURES AND FEELINGS VII

FIGURES AND FEELINGS VIII

Draw a line from each figure to the word that best describes it.
Then draw a new figure for each word.

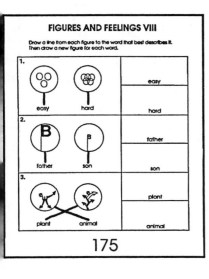

	easy
	hard
	father
	son
	plant
	animal

COLORS AND FEELINGS I

Follow the color key below to color each figure.
Draw a line from each figure to the word that best describes it.
Then make a new figure to represent each word.

O=Orange P=Pink R=Red W=White Blu=Blue Blk=Black Y=Yellow G=Green Brn=Brown

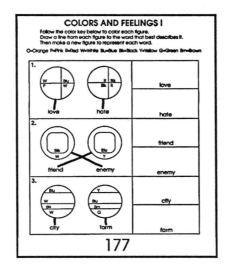

	love
	hate
	friend
	enemy
	city
	farm

COLORS AND FEELINGS II

Follow the color key below to color each figure.
Draw a line from each figure to the word that best describes it.
Then make a new figure to represent each word.

O=Orange P=Pink R=Red W=White Blu=Blue Blk=Black Y=Yellow G=Green Brn=Brown

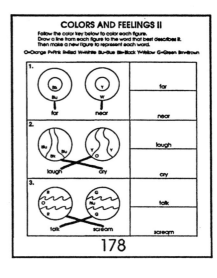

	far
	near
	laugh
	cry
	talk
	scream

COLORS AND FEELINGS III

Follow the color key below to color each figure.
Draw a line from each figure to the word that best describes it.
Then make a new figure to represent each word.

O=Orange P=Pink R=Red W=White Blu=Blue Blk=Black Y=Yellow G=Green Brn=Brown

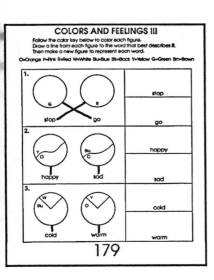

	stop
	go
	happy
	sad
	cold
	warm

COLORS AND FEELINGS IV

Follow the color key below to color each figure.
Draw a line from each figure to the word that best describes it.
Then make a new figure to represent each word.

O=Orange P=Pink R=Red W=White Blu=Blue Blk=Black Y=Yellow G=Green Brn=Brown

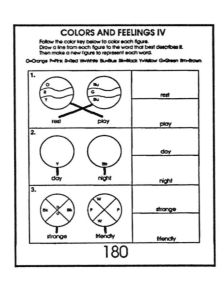

	rest
	play
	day
	night
	strange
	friendly

COLORS AND FEELINGS V

Follow the color key below to color each figure.
Draw a line from each figure to the word that best describes it.
Then make a new figure to represent each word.

O=Orange P=Pink R=Red W=White Blu=Blue Blk=Black Y=Yellow G=Green Brn=Brown

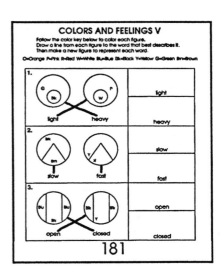

	light
	heavy
	slow
	fast
	open
	closed

COLORS AND FEELINGS VI

Follow the color key below to color each figure.
Draw a line from each figure to the word that best describes it.
Then make a new figure to represent each word.

O=Orange P=Pink R=Red W=White Blu=Blue Blk=Black Y=Yellow G=Green Brn=Brown

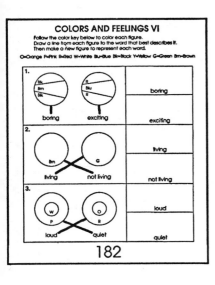

	boring
	exciting
	living
	not living
	loud
	quiet

COLORS AND FEELINGS VII

Follow the color key below to color each figure.
Draw a line from each figure to the word that best describes it.
Then make a new figure to represent each word.

O=Orange P=Pink R=Red W=White Blu=Blue Blk=Black Y=Yellow G=Green Brn=Brown

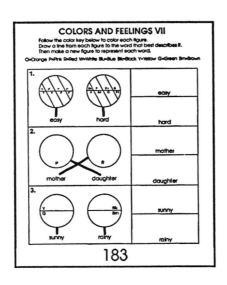

	easy
	hard
	mother
	daughter
	sunny
	rainy

COLORS AND FEELINGS VIII

Follow the color key below to color each figure.
Draw a line from each figure to the word that best describes it.
Then make a new figure to represent each word.

O=Orange P=Pink R=Red W=White Blu=Blue Blk=Black Y=Yellow G=Green Brn=Brown

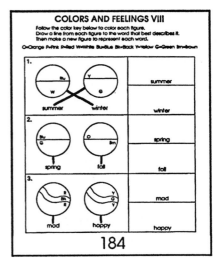

	summer
	winter
	spring
	fall
	mad
	happy

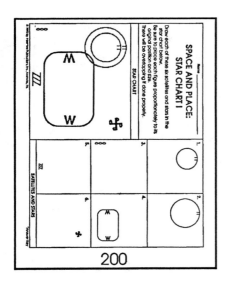

200

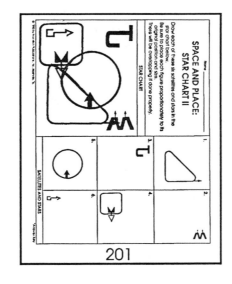

201

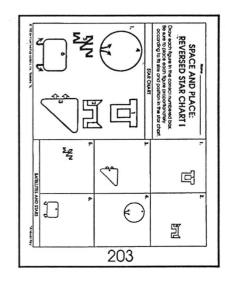

203

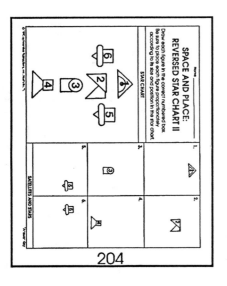

204

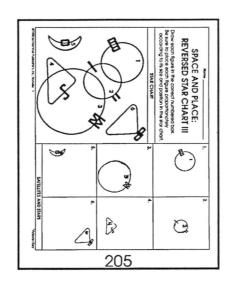

205

Pg 214
3 squares 4 triangles 41 circles

Pg 215

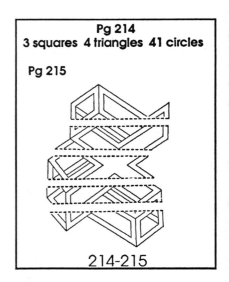

214-215

Pg 216   **Pg 217**

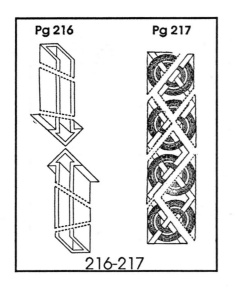

216-217

OP ART: TWO DIMENSIONAL V
Find the seven "holes" in the design and complete the design.
One is done for you.

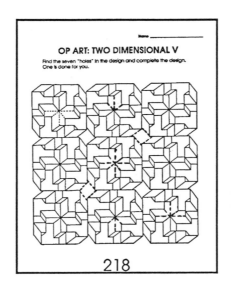

218

OP ART: TWO DIMENSIONAL VI
Finish each design so that it looks exactly like its partner.

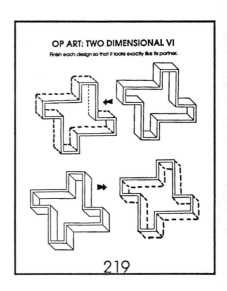

219